DATE DUE

How to use this book

This book has been carefully developed to help you understand the chemistry of the elements. In it you will find a systematic and comprehensive coverage of the basic qualities of each element. Each two-page entry contains information at various levels of technical content and language, along with definitions of useful technical terms, as shown in the thumbnail diagram to the right. There is a comprehensive glossary of technical terms at the back of the book, along with an extensive index, key facts, an explanation of the periodic table, and a description of how to interpret chemical equations.

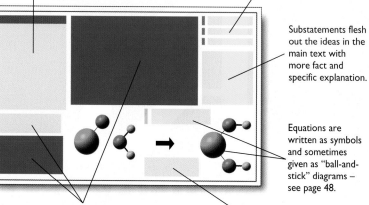

The main text follows the sequence of information in the book and summarizes the concepts presented on the two pages.

Technical definitions.

Substatements flesh out the ideas in the main text with more fact and specific explanation.

Equations are written as symbols and sometimes given as "ball-and-stick" diagrams – see page 48.

Photographs and diagrams have been carefully selected and annotated for clarity.

Also… explains advanced concepts.

Author
Brian Knapp, BSc, PhD
Project consultant
Keith B. Walshaw, MA, BSc, DPhil
        (Head of Chemistry, Leighton Park School)
Industrial consultant
Jack Brettle, BSc, PhD (Chief Research Scientist, Pilkington plc)
Art Director
Duncan McCrae, BSc
Editor
Elizabeth Walker, BA
Special photography
Ian Gledhill
Illustrations
David Woodroffe
Electronic page makeup
Julie James Graphic Design
Designed and produced by
EARTHSCAPE EDITIONS
Print consultants
Landmark Production Consultants Ltd
Reproduced by
Leo Reprographics
Printed in Hong Kong by
Wing King Tong Company Ltd

First published in the United States in 1996 by Grolier Educational, Sherman Turnpike, Danbury, CT 06816

First reprint 1997, second reprint 1997, and third reprint 2000. New and revised edition 2002

Copyright © 1996 & 2002
Atlantic Europe Publishing Company Limited

Cataloging information may be obtained directly from Grolier Educational.

Volumes 1-18 Set ISBN: 0–7172–5674–X
Volume 4 ISBN: 0–7172–7576–0
Library of Congress Number: 95–082222
Dewey: 546—dc21

Acknowledgments
The publishers would like to thank the following for their kind help and advice: *Mr Ah Aia Tan and Guthrie Plantation & Agricultural Sdn Bhd: Mr J. Made Mawa of Budi-Ukir, Mr I. Made Rangun, Pippa Trounce* and *Vauxhall Motors Limited.*

Picture credits
All photographs are from the **Earthscape Editions** photolibrary except the following:
(c=center t=top b=bottom l=left r=right)
Vauxhall Motors Limited 11t, 33b and **ZEFA** 31cl.

Front cover: The chemical reduction of iron oxide to molten iron. At the time this picture was taken the mixture had reached 2,000°C.
Title page: This pyrite crystal shows a characteristic cube structure.

This product is manufactured from sustainable managed forests. For every tree cut down at least one more is planted.

The demonstrations described or illustrated in this book are not for replication. The Publisher cannot accept any responsibility for any accidents or injuries that may result from conducting the experiments described or illustrated in this book.

Contents

Introduction   4

Iron   6

Corrosion of iron: rust   8

The nature of rust   10

Ores of iron   12

Iron oxides   14

Iron colors in the landscape   16

Iron sulfide   18

Iron compounds   20

Refining iron ore: a small-scale demonstration   22

Smelting iron ore   24

The chemistry of smelting   26

Cast and wrought iron   28

Steelmaking   30

Mild steel   32

Special steels   34

Chromium   36

Chromium colors   38

Manganese   40

Potassium permanganate   42

The Periodic Table   44

Understanding equations   46

Key facts about iron, chromium, and manganese   48

Glossary of technical terms   49

Set Index   50

Introduction

An element is a substance that cannot be broken down into a simpler substance by any known means. Each of the 92 naturally occurring elements is therefore one of the fundamental materials from which everything in the Universe is made. This book is about iron, chromium and manganese.

Iron

Iron is one of the world's workhorse elements, found in most of the structures we make, from bridges and skyscrapers to computers and fencing wire.

Iron is cheap to obtain, easy to shape and very strong. For all these reasons it is used more widely than any other metal. But all of the advantages of iron have to be balanced against one major disadvantage: it is a fairly reactive element, prone to rust when exposed to damp air.

Iron (whose chemical symbol, Fe, comes from the Latin *ferrum*) is now one of the most commonly used metals of modern times. But it was not always so. Although the first use of iron dates back some 3,000 years to the period of archeology called the Iron Age, until the last century iron was difficult to find and work and expensive to use.

Pure iron is a soft silvery-gray metal. It can be bent and stretched at room temperature, and at 1,535°C it will melt. This temperature is much higher than the temperature at which wood burns. This explains why earlier civilizations found iron so difficult to use, as they could not produce such high temperatures to work iron.

In fact iron has only been widely available since the Industrial Revolution of the 18th and 19th centuries. At this time, inventors like Abraham Darby learned how to obtain large quantities of iron economically using coke. With iron at last cheap and plentiful, the people of the 19th century turned the world into the engineering age.

Iron is not just found as a metal. Compounds of iron, for example, are found in almost all living things: iron compounds are a vital nutrient for all plants and animals, and they make our blood appear red in color. Iron compounds are also the basis of a rich variety of natural colors, both in rocks and in nature.

Iron, along with very few other elements, possesses the property of magnetism. This property makes iron essential in compasses and inside every electric motor. Indeed, this makes iron one of the most versatile of all the elements.

Chromium

Chromium, whose chemical symbol is Cr, is named after the Greek word for color. It is responsible for both the deep red color of a ruby and the green of emeralds. Chromium is a shiny, rare metal, but because it resists corrosion, it is very important as a surface coating called "chrome plating."

Manganese

Manganese, whose chemical symbol is Mn, is named for the Latin word for magnesia, a magnetic stone. It is a silver-gray metal. Manganese has been identified in great quantities on the deep ocean floor, as yet too deep for collection. Manganese is used for hardening steel and in batteries.

▲ Iron is the coloring in the red hemoglobin molecules of blood cells. Its main function is to carry oxygen around the body.

Foods high in iron content include meat (liver and heart), egg yolk, wheat germ, and most green vegetables.

Some people, such as pregnant women and elderly people, suffer iron deficiency. They have to take extra iron in the form of tablets.

Iron

Iron is a dense, silvery-gray metal. It is the most widely used of all the metal elements because it is common, is cheap to produce from its ores, can be bent while cold, and is strong.

However, some of its properties are less welcome. For example, it is quite reactive, especially with air and water, a process called corrosion. You can see why this happens by looking at the demonstrations below.

The reactivity of iron

Some metals are more reactive than others. Gold, for example, hardly reacts at all, which is why it stays bright and does not tarnish (develop a dull oxide coating). On the other hand, some metals, like potassium, react vigorously with oxygen (corrode) as soon as they are placed in the air.

Metals can be placed in order of how vigorously they react, in a list called a reactivity series (see right).

Copper is near the bottom of the reactivity series, while iron is higher up. Therefore iron will always corrode when placed in a solution containing a copper compound such as copper sulfate. On the other hand, iron is below magnesium, which is why magnesium will always corrode when placed next to iron. This is shown in the picture on the right, where a small strip of magnesium has been wrapped around the shank of an iron nail and placed in a bottle containing water and an indicator.

❶ Iron filings (the dark material) are placed in a small pile in a dish. Copper sulfate (the blue solution) is added.

REACTIVITY SERIES	
Element	*Reactivity*
potassium sodium calcium **magnesium** aluminum manganese chromium zinc **iron** cadmium tin lead **copper** mercury silver gold platinum	*most reactive* *least reactive*

The red color is caused by an indicator in the water. The clear water shows a neutral reaction. As the magnesium corrodes, it produces magnesium hydroxide, an alkali, that turns the region near the corroding magnesium red.

❷ After a while a number of changes have occurred because the iron filings have reacted with the copper sulfate. There is no acid or other chemical here.

Notice how the solution has become a very pale green. The edges of the iron filings have changed to a reddish-brown (coppery) color, looking a little like a reef fringing a coral island.

The reason for the changes is that a chemical reaction has occurred. Some of the iron has gone into solution. The copper "reef" has been deposited (precipitated) out of the solution onto the iron filings.

The copper in the copper sulfate makes the solution blue; iron sulfate solutions are green, so the green color shows that the copper and iron have "swapped," and the solution is now iron sulfate.

However, not all of the iron has reacted. There is far more iron than copper, so a complete swap cannot be achieved. If the iron were placed in a huge vat of copper sulfate, it would eventually react entirely and disappear.

Also...

This demonstration uses iron filings, the kind of "swarf" that might be produced as waste from a metal lathe. If a large mass of iron is present as iron filings, there is a larger surface area than if it were present in a big block. As a result, chemical reactions will happen more quickly.

cathodic protection: the technique of making the object that is to be protected from corrosion into the cathode of a cell. For example, a material, such as steel, is protected by coupling it with a more reactive metal, such as magnesium. Steel forms the cathode and magnesium the anode. Zinc protects steel in the same way.

corrosion: the *slow* decay of a substance resulting from contact with gases and liquids in the environment. The term is often applied to metals. Rust is the corrosion of iron.

reactivity: the tendency of a substance to react with other substances. The term is most widely used in comparing the reactivity of metals. Metals are arranged in a reactivity series.

solution: a mixture of a liquid and at least one other substance (e.g., saltwater). Mixtures can be separated by physical means, for example, by evaporation and cooling.

EQUATION: Reaction between iron and copper sulfate

Iron + copper sulfate ⇨ iron sulfate + copper

$$Fe(s) + CuSO_4(aq) \Rightarrow FeSO_4(aq) + Cu(s)$$

Corrosion of iron: rust

The environment is a hazardous place for materials. Even in "clean" country air, materials will slowly show signs of surface change because of the effects of water and gases in the air. The change in the surface of materials is a reaction with oxygen in the air. It is called corrosion and produces a coating called an oxide.

Iron is particularly susceptible to corrosion, known as rusting, in damp air or oxygen-rich water because it is a reactive material.

▼ This jar is called a desiccator. The blue crystals in the bottom are silica gel colored with cobalt chloride. They absorb any moisture in the air. The nails are therefore in completely dry air. Although they have been sealed in this desiccator for many years, they show no signs of rust. This indicates that both moisture and oxygen are required to form rust.

▲ Steel nails need water and oxygen from the air to rust quickly. This is because pure water is a poor corroding agent. When oxygen is present, such as when water is left uncovered, nails left in water will rust (oxidize) very rapidly.

Iron's special oxide layers

The materials that most often show signs of corrosion are metals. The oxide coating that develops on the surface of some metals is so thin it is invisible.

Look at a clean iron or steel nail, and the surface looks unaffected because the oxide layer is so thin. When the oxide coating is thicker, it may appear as a discoloring, or tarnishing, of the surface.

However, unlike some other metals such as aluminum and copper, iron's oxide coating is not able to keep water and oxygen out. On the contrary, it is a porous coating, which is why it rusts.

corrosion: the *slow* decay of a substance resulting from contact with gases and liquids in the environment. The term is often applied to metals. Rust is the corrosion of iron.

oxide: a compound that includes oxygen and one other element.

porous: a material containing many small holes or cracks. Quite often the pores are connected, and liquids, such as water or oil, can move through them.

product: a substance produced by a chemical reaction.

◄ Old iron anchoring chain and a new galvanized chain.
▼ The anchor chain is not attacked evenly. The surface of the iron is pitted in places and shows rust scales in other places.

▼ This rusty bolt shows many of the features of corrosion. Notice, for example, how the thread is much less clear. This is because when iron corrodes (rusts), oxygen and iron combine to make a bulkier substance than pure iron. So, as the sides of the threads rust and swell, the gap between threads becomes smaller. This is one reason why a rusty bolt is so hard to undo: the oxide has jammed the threads.

The nature of rust

When a material rusts, it is because water and oxygen have combined with the metal iron. To understand what happens, chemists think about how the tiniest particles – the atoms – of each element behave when they react.

The unrusty iron is made of small heavy atoms that pack tightly together. The water is a molecule made of one oxygen atom and two hydrogen atoms. The oxygen gas is made up of pairs of oxygen atoms.

When rusting occurs on the surface of a material, the atoms split up and regroup. The combination of several different sizes of atoms is a bulkier and less dense material than pure iron, and it easily flakes off.

▼ Large structures like the Sydney Harbor bridge need to be painted constantly to prevent them from corroding away. Even so, corrosion in exposed places is difficult to prevent.

Rust and its prevention

Iron or mild steel, water and the oxygen in air combine to cause rust. It is one of the most common chemical reactions around us. Rusting occurs even in damp air – no actual droplets of water are needed – and even more quickly in air that has impurities in it. Impurities can include sea salt (which is one reason ships and iron objects near the sea rust so easily) and also pollution gases (such as may be found in cities and near factories or power stations). Sulfur dioxide (present in acid rain) is a particularly effective pollutant because it dissolves in water droplets to form sulfurous acid.

We use iron and steel in all manner of objects because it is cheap, strong and plentiful. To counteract rusting, iron is protected with paint or another metal such as zinc (when it is called galvanized iron).

▼ All iron and steel objects have to be painted or protected in some other way against rust. Most vehicles are coated in a number of protective layers during manufacture and given several coats of paint before they leave the factory.

electrode: a conductor that forms one terminal of a cell.

electrolysis: an electrical-chemical process that uses an electric current to cause the breakup of a compound and the movement of metal ions in a solution. The process happens in many natural situations (as for example in rusting) and is also commonly used in industry for purifying (refining) metals or for plating metal objects with a fine, even metal coating.

electrolyte: a solution that conducts electricity.

oxidation/reduction: a reaction in which oxygen is gained or lost. (Also… More generally oxidation involves the loss of electrons.)

EQUATION: The rusting of iron

Iron + water + oxygen ⇨ ferric hydroxide ⇨ ferric oxide + water

$$4Fe(s) + 6H_2O(l) + 3O_2(g) \Rightarrow 4Fe(OH)_3(s) \Rightarrow 2Fe_2O_3(s) + 6H_2O(l)$$
Rust

Also...
How iron becomes pitted

If a wetted iron surface is exposed either by being uncoated or because the paint on the surface has been chipped, oxygen atoms are able to enter the water through its surface skin. In this water one of the world's tiniest batteries forms. The water is oxygen rich and the iron forms an electrode, one terminal of a battery. The oxygen-poor region in the scratch, and thus farther from the air, forms the other electrode. The water forms the electrolyte. A minute electric current now flows, and iron is carried in solution to the oxygen-rich water, where it is oxidized and deposited.

Thus, iron is removed from one part of the metal and deposited as an oxide or hydroxide nearby. This explains why rusty material is often both pitted and lumpy.

(To find out more about the way electrolysis and electroplating work, see page 37.)

▶ This rusting horseshoe shows two forms of rust. The light brown rust patches are recently formed ferric hydroxide or $Fe(OH)_3$. In contrast, the darker-brown rust patches are the final solid state of ferric oxide, or Fe_2O_3, shown in the equation above.

Ores of iron

Iron is the second most abundant metal (after aluminum) in the Earth's crust. However, pure iron is seldom found in nature. Most often it is found in the ore called hematite (which contains one-third of its weight as iron) and magnetite (with about two-thirds of its weight as iron). These compounds, both containing iron and oxygen, are known as iron oxides.

Magnetite

Iron is famous for its ability to act as a magnet or to be attracted by magnets. Native (pure) iron as well as iron alloys such as steel and iron compounds such as some iron oxides (for example, the ore magnetite) are also magnetic. The property is created because each tiny crystal of iron can behave as a magnet, organizing itself into the same direction as all those crystals nearby.

The earliest knowledge of the magnetic properties of iron comes from the strongly magnetic rock known as lodestone or magnetite. The word magnetite comes from the region called Magnesia in Greece, where lodestone was mined in ancient times.

A ball-shaped piece of lodestone has two regions where it will attract or repel other ball-shaped lodestones. These places are known as the magnetic poles.

▶ This piece of magnetite has been dipped in iron filings to demonstrate it has magnetic properties. Magnetite is Fe_3O_4.

Meteorites

Meteorites are one of the few highly concentrated sources of iron ore. In some meteorites iron occurs as uncombined metal (called native metal).

Because the majority of all meteorites are about nine-tenths iron, they require relatively little purifying, and for this reason they were prized by earlier civilizations. Huge craters where meteorites had fallen were an obvious site to find native iron.

In ancient times, iron was known as the "metal of heaven." This may be because people saw meteorites fall and then discovered that they contained almost pure iron. The first iron used was definitely from meteorites, like the one that created the giant Meteor Crater in Arizona.

Hematite

This is the name for the most widespread form of iron ore. It is most often found in rocks once deposited by rivers or the sea.

The deep red color of some rocks indicates that they contain hematite. Most of these rocks were formed in parts of the tropics with wet and dry seasons. During the wet season the minerals eroded from the land were washed to basins, deltas or coasts. During the dry period the water evaporated, the sediments dried out and iron compounds oxidized to iron oxide. These rocks are often referred to as "red beds" and are usually fine-grained materials such as shales.

▲ A piece of iron ore (hematite). The deep red color is due to the fact that hematite is iron oxide. Pure iron forms the gray-colored crystals. Hematite is Fe_2O_3.

Limonite

Limonite is an iron oxide that forms in cooler climates than hematite. It is usually yellow, orange and brown rather than red. It contains water molecules and so is an example of a hydrous (water-containing) iron oxide.

Limonite is often found in marshes and is thus also known as bog iron ore.

The water content influences the color of the oxide. Heating limonite causes the water to be driven off, thus darkening the color of the oxide and yielding the paint color "burnt ocher." In fact, it was traditionally used as a source of ocher pigments in paint.

Iron oxides

Iron oxide can occur in two forms, depending on how much oxygen is bound with the iron. Compounds of iron with a lower oxygen content are known as ferrous compounds, whereas compounds of iron with a higher oxygen content are known as ferric compounds.

Ferrous compounds

The color of the iron compound is related to the amount of oxygen it contains. Ferrous compounds (also known as Iron II compounds) have a green, gray or blue color.

The dirty-looking green gelatinous precipitate in the bottom of the tube on the right is a ferrous hydroxide (iron II hydroxide).

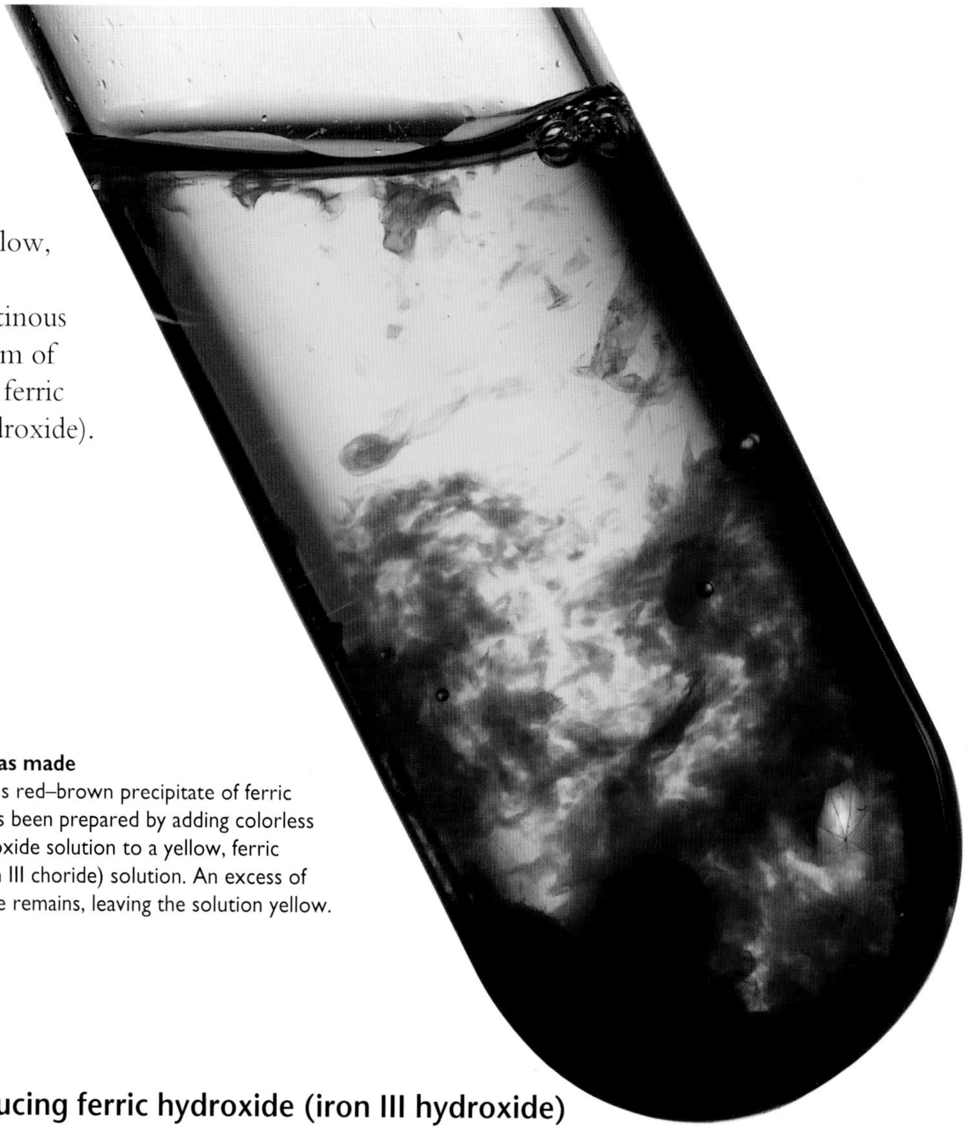

Ferric compounds

Ferric compounds (also known as iron III compounds) have a yellow, red or brown color.

The red-brown gelatinous precipitate in the bottom of the tube shown here is ferric hydroxide (iron III hydroxide).

▶ **How it was made**
The gelatinous red–brown precipitate of ferric hydroxide has been prepared by adding colorless sodium hydroxide solution to a yellow, ferric chloride (iron III choride) solution. An excess of ferric chloride remains, leaving the solution yellow.

EQUATION: Producing ferric hydroxide (iron III hydroxide)

Sodium hydroxide + iron III chloride ⇨ iron III hydroxide + sodium chloride

$$3NaOHaq) \quad + \quad FeCl_3(aq) \quad ⇨ \quad Fe(OH)_3(s) \quad + \quad 3NaCl(aq)$$

Drops of sodium hydroxide being released from a dropper.

Also...

Many other iron compounds have striking colors. They have been known and used since ancient times.

Ocher

Ocher is the name given to yellow-red colors produced by iron compounds. Ocher is a powder made by crushing many iron-rich ores. Limonite and hematite (see page 13) produce yellow and red coloring, respectively. If either of these ores is roasted, the colors will darken to red-brown. This is called burnt ocher. The powder is used in paints as the coloring agent or pigment. It is mixed with a liquid before being applied.

Prussian blue

Prussian blue (so named because it was developed in Prussia during the 18th century) is obtained by reacting iron oxide with potassium ferrocyanide. It is used as a "whitener" in laundry detergents, a light blue dye giving the optical illusion of whiteness to clothes. In more concentrated form it acts as a blue pigment in paints and enamels.

Gelatinous drop-shaped precipitated solid forms as the drop of sodium hydroxide falls into the solution containing ferrous sulfate.

▶ How it was made

The green gelatinous precipitate of ferrous hydroxide (iron II hydroxide) was prepared by adding colorless sodium hydroxide solution to ferrous sulfate (iron II sulfate) solution.

EQUATION: Producing ferrous hydroxide (iron II hydroxide)

Sodium hydroxide + iron II chloride ⇨ iron II hydroxide + sodium chloride

$$2NaOH(aq) \quad + \quad FeCl_2(aq) \quad ⇨ \quad Fe(OH)_2(s) \quad + \quad 2NaCl(aq)$$

Iron colors in the landscape

Much of the color in the world's rocks and soils is produced by iron compounds. These colors allow geologists and soil scientists to tell much about the way the rocks and soils of the world have formed.

Deep red colors tell of iron that was oxidized in hot, tropical conditions; oranges and yellows tell of iron oxides formed in cooler climates; while grays, blues and greens are produced when iron compounds are short of oxygen, such as deep under the sea.

Soils formed from these rocks often have a color similar to the rock on which they have formed. However, when soils are affected by acid waters, iron is removed into solution, and the rock becomes dramatically paler in color.

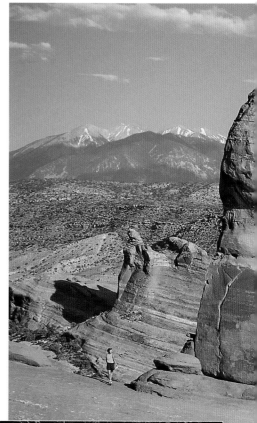

Iron and soils

Iron compounds are important constituents of soils and responsible for many soil colors. In some parts of the world they are also responsible for poor drainage and a variety of other soil problems.

Soils are colored by a combination of iron oxides and organic matter. Most organic matter occurs close to the surface. Its black color makes the topsoil a darker color than any other part of the soil.

In some cases, such as when a soil receives large amounts of rainfall, the organic matter reacts with the rainwater to produce acids that are strong enough to dissolve the iron compounds. When this happens, the iron compounds, which provide the brown, orange, red and yellow colors in a soil, are removed and the soil layer turns ashen gray. The ashen gray color is the color of the quartz sand and clay particles that remain.

In regions lower down in the soil, the acid conditions are less intense and the iron compounds are reprecipitated. Here the iron concentrates to produce a strong orange color.

▲ Soils change color through their profiles, in part because iron is carried by acid waters, as shown in this spodosol from New Zealand.

acidity: a general term for the strength of an acid in a solution.

oxide: a compound that includes oxygen and one other element.

solution: a mixture of a liquid and at least one other substance (e.g., saltwater). Mixtures can be separated by physical means, for example, by evaporation and cooling.

◄ The reddish-colored banding of this sandstone shows that these rocks were formed in hot conditions. The variation in color shows that some materials were formed in more iron-rich environments than others. This is Delicate Arch, Arches National Park, Utah.

Laterite

Most tropical soils have a deep red color, which is the result of weathering of iron compounds in climates with high temperatures.

Laterite is the name given to a soil material that is found in some tropical regions with a long dry season followed by long wet season.

A laterite layer is a thick zone containing iron and aluminum oxides and very little else. This unusual material is so rich in iron compounds that it is mined as an iron ore.

Most laterites are very old. It is believed that they result from the effect of large amounts of water washing through a tropical soil. Under these conditions the silica that makes up the body of sand and clay particles (normally not a soluble material) goes into solution, so that the iron and aluminum compounds remain behind and so become more concentrated.

While still in the soil, laterite layers are soft; but when they are exposed to the air, such as when a road cutting is made, they oxidize and quickly become rock hard.

◄ This laterite soil from Queensland in Australia is very deep and on exposure to air becomes very hard.

Iron sulfide

Iron sulfide, or pyrite, is a common compound of iron, also known as "fool's gold." Pyrite is a very common mineral, occurring in many types of rock. It is commonly found in veins and can form perfect cubic (cube-shaped) crystals.

Shale rocks contain pyrite because the muds from which they are formed were once also combined with decaying organic matter. As the organic matter decayed, it took oxygen from the water, and hydrogen sulfide gas was produced. The hydrogen sulfide reacted with iron in the water to produce iron sulfide. In the right conditions the iron sulfide grew into perfect cubic crystals; in other circumstances it developed into nodules.

Iron sulfide is not stable in damp air, where it readily oxidizes to a brown color. The shiny crystal that you see in the picture on the right will turn progressively gray and begin to crumble to iron sulfate.

Iron sulfide is not used as an iron ore, because its high sulfur content is difficult to remove. It is mainly used in the production of sulfuric acid.

A cubic crystal of pyrite. The parallel "scratches," known as striations, are a common feature of pyrite crystals.

▶ This is a typical sample of an ore. The conditions that allow the formation of pyrite are also right for the formation of crystals of other compounds. This is the reason refining ores is often a very complicated chemical process.

These transparent crystals are quartz.

The dark crystals are sphalerite (zinc sulfide).

◀ A cubic crystal of
pyrite or iron sulfide.

ion: an atom, or group of atoms, that has gained or
lost one or more electrons and so developed an
electrical charge.

pyrite: "mineral of fire". This name comes from the
fact that pyrite (iron sulfide) will give off sparks if
struck with a stone.

sulfide: a sulfur compound that contains no oxygen.

Cubic structure

In a pyrite cube an iron ion occurs at each corner of the
cube and the middle of each of the faces. A pair of sulfur
ions are found halfway along each edge.

The bonds between the iron and sulfur ions are very
strong, and they cannot be deformed. This gives the
pyrite the property of being hard and brittle.

▼ A diagrammatic
representation of the
cubic structure of pyrite.

▼ This bottle used to contain
about 10 pyrite cubes. During 20
years of exposure to humid air
the pyrite has weathered to leave
a gray residue of iron sulfate.

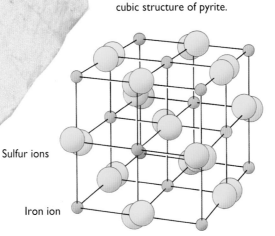

Sulfur ions

Iron ion

EQUATION: Weathering of pyrite (iron sulfide) in damp air

Iron sulfide + water + oxygen from the air ⇨ iron sulfate + sulfuric acid

$$2FeS_2(s) \quad + \quad 2H_2O(l) \quad + \quad 7O_2(s) \quad ⇨ \quad 2FeSO_4(s) \quad + \quad 2H_2SO_4(aq)$$

◀▶ Pyrite nodules are commonly
found in rocks such as chalk.
They consist of radiating crystals of
iron sulfide, the ends of which can
clearly be seen in the picture on the
left. The surface is brown because
the iron has oxidized. However, in
the picture on the right the change
from sulfide to sulfate inside the
nodule is causing it to break up.

Iron compounds

Iron is well known for its magnetic qualities, its ability to bend under pressure and its tendency to get rusty in air. But just how many, if any, of these characteristics are inherited by iron compounds?

The relationship of iron compounds to iron can be investigated by mixing iron and sulfur. The results of heating the mixture are described here.

❶▼ Iron and sulfur form distinctively colored powders. When mixed, the dark brown iron can be seen speckling the yellow sulfur.

Iron filings   Sulfur   Mixture of iron filings and sulfur

Iron filings separated by magnet

Mixture of iron filings and sulfur

❷▲ Iron is magnetic, so a magnet will draw the iron from the iron-sulfur mixture. At room temperature the mixture can thus easily be separated.

❸▲ If the mixture is heated strongly with a Bunsen flame, as shown above, it will begin to glow red.

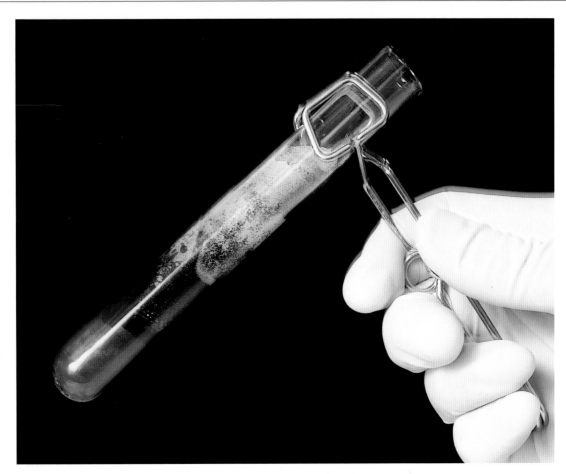

4 ▲ The tube can then be taken from the flame, and the red glow will spread up the tube without further heating. This is because the chemical reaction taking place, caused by heating, itself releases heat that in turn keeps the reaction going as long as there is still elemental iron and sulfur in the tube.

5 ▶ When the reaction is over, there is a brown cokelike compound in the tube. This is iron sulfide. Compare it with the crystals on the previous page to see that compounds can have the same chemical formula but look remarkably different. Iron sulfide has no magnetic properties, showing that the compound shares little in common with the starting materials from which it was made.

When heated in a test tube, the iron and sulfur combine to form the compound iron sulfide, which has no magnetic properties.

EQUATION: Laboratory production of iron sulfide

Iron + sulfur ⇨ iron sulfide

$Fe(s) + S(s) ⇨ FeS(s)$

Refining iron ore: a small-scale demonstration

Iron oxide will not react at room temperature. This is why a piece of iron oxide rock will simply sit on your window ledge forever.

In common with many chemical reactions, you need to put in a lot of heat energy to make iron oxide react with other chemicals.

In the demonstration shown on this page, the principle of generating heat by chemical reactions is shown.

The apparatus

A container (in this case a plant pot with a hole in the bottom, because it is cheap and it only melts at very high temperatures) is filled with a mixture of aluminum powder and iron oxide (iron ore) powder. A small cup-shaped indentation is made in the top of the mixture, and some barium peroxide powder is added. A fuse of magnesium ribbon is buried in the top of the mixture.

▲ The magnesium ribbon fuse is lighted.

Also...

This demonstration shows that materials can be made to react at high temperatures even if they are completely unreactive at low temperatures. A modified form of this demonstration is used to weld rails as they are laid. A bag filled with the powder is tied around the rail sections to be welded and the fuse lighted. The rest happens automatically!

The demonstration also shows the principle of extracting iron from its ore. It requires a chemical reaction to strip the oxygen from the iron. However, the use of the equipment shown here is not practical for industrial purposes. Instead, charcoal or coke is used, as shown on pages 24 and 25.

Magnesium ribbon burns with an intense heat when lighted and so makes a good fuse.

Mixture of aluminum and iron oxide. At room temperature this mixture is completely unreactive.

Earthenware plant pot

▶ This unpromising earthenware plant pot contains the ingredients for a spectacular chemical reaction.

> ### WARNING
> *This demonstration produces materials with a temperature of 2,000°C and must never be attempted by anyone except a qualified chemist.*

Barium peroxide contains a good supply of oxygen to help the magnesium release heat.

EQUATION: Chemical reduction of iron oxide to iron

Iron oxide + aluminum ⇨ iron metal + aluminum oxide

$$Fe_2O_3(s) \quad + \quad 2Al(s) \quad ⇨ \quad 2Fe(s) \quad + \quad Al_2O_3(s)$$

How it works

1 The whole apparatus is placed out in a field, well away from any inflammable materials. The fuse is lighted. The magnesium burns with a brilliant white light. The fuse burns down into the barium peroxide, causing it to decompose, thus releasing oxygen. Enough heat energy is released to bring the aluminum powder up to the temperature at which it will react.

2 As soon as the aluminum powder is hot enough, it reacts with oxygen from the iron oxide, releasing more heat. This causes the aluminum to form aluminum oxide, a lightweight fine, powder that is easily carried aloft by the rising currents of heated air. This is what appears as a white smoke.

3 The reacting aluminum raises the temperature of the iron oxide to about 2,000°C. Because the aluminum takes the oxygen from the iron oxide, the iron metal can flow freely.

4 Iron is heavy, so it sinks through the mixture, flowing out of the hole in the bottom of the plant pot.

5 The molten iron is collected in a pot filled with water and sand to cool it and prevent it burning its way into the soil below! The water in the container goes up in steam as soon as the iron flows into it, adding to the spectacular effect.

▲▶ The magnesium ribbon heats the barium oxide, starting an intense reaction that releases oxygen and enough heat to ignite the mixture of iron and aluminum. The temperature of the mixture reaches 2,000°C and molten iron is released. This falls out of the bottom of the plant pot and is captured in a bath of water. The water in the bath is immediately turned to steam.

23

Smelting iron ore

Processing, or smelting, of iron ore is done in a blast furnace, a tall oven designed to produce the high temperatures needed to melt and refine iron oxide.

In essence the furnace has to remove the oxygen from the metal ore (the ore must be reduced), and the waste rock must be separated from the valuable metal. This is done with a very hot blast of carbon monoxide gas. The whole furnace is built so that hot carbon monoxide gas is continuously produced and blown through melting rock. The heavy slag and molten iron escape from the bottom of the furnace, and a charge of new ore and fuel is applied at the top. In this way the blast furnace can be operated continuously.

▲ A modern integrated iron and steel plant. The raw materials lying on the dockside in front of the furnace are introduced to the top of the furnace by a conveyor system.

▶ Making iron on a large scale was one of the foundations of the modern industrial world. Giant iron furnaces were built at the heart of many industrial cities.

Over the years, the furnaces became hemmed in by the city, so they moved to sites outside the cities. At the same time, they became larger, so that fewer furnaces could make all the iron needed. This picture shows what an iron furnace looked like in the 19th century.

The modern blast furnace: chemistry in action

Modern blast furnaces are designed to run continuously. They are charged with a mixture of iron ore, coke and limestone at the top of the furnace. Each ton of iron uses up about three-quarters of a ton of coke and a quarter of a ton of limestone.

The blast furnace is designed so that a number of different chemical reactions can occur as the charge moves down through the furnace.

The charge becomes hotter as it moves down, until it melts in the lowest region of the furnace. Iron and waste materials (slag) separate as they melt and are drawn off from the bottom of the furnace.

The iron produced this way is called pig iron. It is the foundation material for other kinds of iron and steel. It is rarely used without further chemical treatment because it is hard and brittle. Cast iron, slightly refined pig iron, can only be used in places where the iron receives little impact or shaking. Cast iron was used as the material for many early iron bridges; steel is used in modern structures.

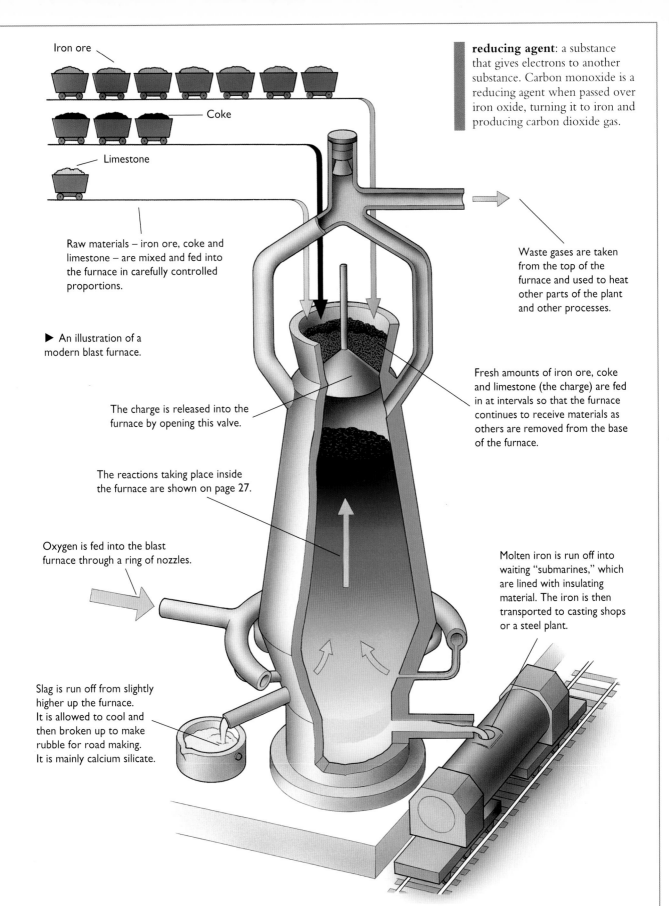

Iron ore

Coke

Limestone

reducing agent: a substance that gives electrons to another substance. Carbon monoxide is a reducing agent when passed over iron oxide, turning it to iron and producing carbon dioxide gas.

Raw materials – iron ore, coke and limestone – are mixed and fed into the furnace in carefully controlled proportions.

▶ An illustration of a modern blast furnace.

The charge is released into the furnace by opening this valve.

The reactions taking place inside the furnace are shown on page 27.

Oxygen is fed into the blast furnace through a ring of nozzles.

Slag is run off from slightly higher up the furnace. It is allowed to cool and then broken up to make rubble for road making. It is mainly calcium silicate.

Waste gases are taken from the top of the furnace and used to heat other parts of the plant and other processes.

Fresh amounts of iron ore, coke and limestone (the charge) are fed in at intervals so that the furnace continues to receive materials as others are removed from the base of the furnace.

Molten iron is run off into waiting "submarines," which are lined with insulating material. The iron is then transported to casting shops or a steel plant.

The chemistry of smelting

The processes that occur inside the blast furnace are quite complex, and different reactions happen at the top and bottom of the furnace.

The objective is to ensure that the right chemical reactions occur in each part of the furnace so that controlled and continuous processing is achieved. The reactions involved in the general principles of iron-making (shown on the previous page) are described here.

After the last reaction, the iron that flows from the bottom of the furnace into the molds (known as pigs) is about 95% iron, with various proportions of carbon and other impurities.

The waste gases pass out through pipes at the top of the furnace.

Cold iron ore, coke and limestone are added as a charge into the top of the furnace.

Slag

The limestone in the charge decomposes to calcium oxide and gives off carbon dioxide gas. The calcium oxide reacts with the nonmetal of the ore. For example, it reacts with the silica of the rock to make calcium silicate.

The mixture of rock materials is known as slag. It is a light gray-colored material, less dense than the iron, that is tapped off the furnace from holes above those used to tap the molten iron.

◄ This picture shows a blast furnace with a pile of slag in front of it. The slag will be allowed to cool and then carried away to be made into useful road-making materials.

The slag, less dense than the iron, is tapped off.

Carbon monoxide: the reducing agent

Carbon monoxide gas is produced at the bottom of the furnace. As air is blown in, the coke, which is almost entirely carbon, is oxidized to produce carbon dioxide gas.

Solid carbon plus oxygen gas from the air react to yield carbon dioxide gas, also giving out heat.

As the carbon dioxide bubbles up the furnace, it reacts with more of the coke in the mixture, changing to carbon monoxide gas. This gas then reacts with the iron oxide in the middle of the furnace to yield liquid iron.

ore: a rock containing enough of a useful substance to make mining it worthwhile.

reducing agent: a substance that gives electrons to another substance. Carbon monoxide is a reducing agent in a blast furnace.

slag: a mixture of substances that are waste products of a furnace. Most slags are composed mainly of silicates.

Gases pass up through the mixture in the furnace.

Liquids descend through the mixture in the furnace.

EQUATION: Oxidation of coke

carbon + oxygen ⇨ carbon dioxide

$$C(s) \quad + \quad O_2(g) \quad \Rightarrow \quad CO_2(g)$$

EQUATION: Carbon dioxide reduced

carbon dioxide + carbon ⇨ carbon monoxide

$$CO_2(g) \quad + \quad C(s) \quad \Rightarrow \quad 2CO(s)$$

Carbon monoxide reacts with iron ore to produce molten iron and carbon dioxide gas. The molten iron sinks to the bottom of the furnace.

The oxygen reacts with the coke to produce carbon dioxide gas, which in turn reacts with more of the coke to produce carbon monoxide.

Iron ore to iron metal

Iron oxide sinks down the furnace where it reacts with carbon monoxide gas coming up from the bottom of the furnace. The two then react to produce carbon dioxide gas and liquid iron.

Oxygen gas is pumped in.

EQUATION: Iron oxide is reduced

Iron oxide + carbon monoxide ⇨ iron metal + carbon dioxide

$$Fe_2O_3(s) \quad + \quad 3CO(g) \quad \Rightarrow \quad 2Fe(l) \quad + \quad 3CO_2(g)$$

The molten iron, which is densest, is tapped off as pig iron.

◄ When the iron is tapped from the bottom of the furnace, it is often transferred into "submarines." These insulated containers take the molten iron to the nearby steel furnace for conversion to steel. This process is explained on pages 30 and 31.

Cast and wrought iron

The molten iron that comes from a furnace is known as pig iron. This can be run off into molds to produce a variety of intricate shapes, collectively known as wrought iron. If pig iron is remelted and cooled, it forms cast iron. The plant in which castings are made is called a foundry.

Iron refined in a furnace is not entirely pure, as it contains carbon. The amount of carbon affects the properties of the iron to a large extent. Wrought iron is nearly pure iron, with a carbon content of less than 0.035%. This makes it a relatively soft material that is easily worked with hammers (it is said to be easily forged).

Cast iron has a carbon content above 3%, which makes it harder than wrought iron but much more brittle. If cast iron is cooled quickly, hard but brittle white cast iron is formed; if it is cooled slowly, soft but tough gray cast iron is formed.

Wrought iron

Wrought iron is nearly pure iron, with a soft, fibrous structure. This allows it to be formed into intricate shapes, whether hot or cold. It was used to make everything from plowshares to rifles, from railway track to decorative grills.

Wrought iron replaced bronze in ancient civilizations and led to the Iron Age. It was originally formed simply by hammering the nearly molten ore to remove the impurities.

All the ironwork in old buildings is wrought iron. Cast iron was only made after the mid-18th century when it replaced wrought iron because it is stronger and can be used more easily. In particular, less material is needed for structural purposes, such as bridges and buildings. Wrought iron continued to be used for railway tracks until it was replaced by steel.

▶ The world's first iron bridge, built across the River Severn in England in 1778, ushered in the new Iron Age. It was made of wrought-iron metal. The fastenings are iron wedges rather than rivets because, at this stage, designers were still making bridges of wood and they had not yet learned the technique of riveting.

▲ An 18th-century iron foundry.

Types of cast iron

Cast iron varies according to its silicon and carbon content. Gray cast iron is the most common. It is easily cast and machined, and is used for casting vehicle engine blocks.

To change the properties of gray cast iron into other forms, it must be remelted and the chemical composition altered. Alternatively, some changes can be produced by controlling the rate at which the iron cools after casting.

The uses of cast iron

Cast iron was first introduced as a structural material in the late 18th century. The first buildings to benefit from this new material were factories, where heavy machinery could now be supported on castiron columns. Warehouses were also quick to use and display this new material.

The idea of supporting a building with castiron frames was of vital importance to modern society because it led to the development of high-rise (skyscraper) frame construction in the 20th century. But some of the most flamboyant uses of the metal were in combination with glass panels to make intricately-patterned windows. These were used for railway stations and great exhibition halls such as London's Crystal Palace (built 1851).

For many centuries, ironmakers had made intricate metal objects by working wrought iron with great skill. The mass production of castiron decorative wares allowed much cheaper production. Eventually the skills of many of these ironworkers were lost.

◀ In the 19th century it became very fashionable to use cast iron as a decorative part of architecture. Many railway stations and other large public buildings show an enormous range of uses for cast iron. However, it was used to great effect in many domestic buildings as well. One of the world's most famous uses of cast iron in buildings is seen on these Sydney houses, where exquisitely produced cast iron decorates many of the townhouses of the period. The cast iron is protected from weathering by paint.

Steelmaking

Steel is mostly made of iron, but many of the impurities have been taken out, and controlled amounts of other compounds have been added.

Iron contains about 5% carbon and small amounts of manganese, silicon, phosphorus and sulfur. The steelmaking process aims to reduce the carbon level to below 1.75% by oxidizing iron with oxygen from the air.

Refining the steel

Steel furnaces are the first step in steelmaking. The charge material is collected in a giant steel furnace, where a jet of inert gas such as argon is blown through it so that the steel is stirred and made more uniform. It may then be treated to reduce sulfur and other impurity levels even further. Only then does it go to the mills to be rolled into sheets or made into shapes such as girders, bars and wire.

Also...

The electric arc process is another way to produce molten steel, but it is essentially a melting process for scrap steel, and chemical reactions do not play a major part in it.

▼ The basic oxygen furnace process of steelmaking.

A jet of oxygen is blown over the molten metal.

Molten pig iron, scrap steel and lime are loaded into the furnace.

The furnace can rotate

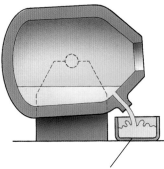

When the reaction is complete the furnace is tilted to pour steel into ladles.

EQUATION: Iron is oxidized, releasing heat

Iron + oxygen ⇨ iron oxide

$$2Fe(s) + O_2(g) \Rightarrow 2FeO(s)$$
<small>heat is released</small>

EQUATION: Silicon impurities are oxidized using lime

Iron oxide + silicon + lime ⇨ steel + slag

$$2FeO(s) + Si(s) + CaO(s) \Rightarrow 2Fe(s) + CaSiO_3(s)$$

EQUATION: Excess carbon in the iron is removed

Iron oxide + carbon in the iron ⇨ steel + carbon monoxide gas

$$FeO(s) + C(s) \Rightarrow Fe(s) + CO(g)$$

Steel-rolling mills

The steel furnace

Just as the iron-making process is chemistry on a grand scale, so too is the steelmaking process.

The steel furnace is where the charge of scrap steel and iron is heated, and where the chemical reactions occur. The first steel furnace was the Bessemer converter, invented by Henry Bessemer in the 1850s. It uses a large pot lined with a basic material such as limestone (calcium carbonate). A blast of air is introduced into the molten iron, causing the iron to oxidize and release a large amount of heat.

As the temperature in the steel furnace rises, the limestone decomposes, releasing calcium oxide. The impurities in the iron react with the calcium oxides to form a molten slag. At this stage the furnace "blows": huge flames appear at the furnace mouth, and gases boil up through the liquid metal.

The oxygen from the iron combines with excess carbon in the iron, oxidizing it to carbon monoxide. In this way the high carbon content of the iron is lowered, and impurities left in the iron from the blast furnace stage are removed.

The Bessemer converter has been improved and is now called the basic oxygen furnace process. However, the chemical reactions that take place remain the same.

oxidation: a reaction in which the oxidizing agent removes electrons.

▲ Sir Henry Bessemer.

▲ This engraving shows a Bessemer converter in use in the last century.

▼ An integrated iron and steel plant, such as this one in Port Kembla, New South Wales can be regarded as a giant chemical plant.

▲ Inside a steel-rolling mill.

Steel furnace

Blast furnace

Raw materials on the dock side.

Mild steel

Mild steel – steel with a carbon content of about 0.25% – is one of the most widely used materials today. It is strong and readily available. Its main drawback is that it is a reactive metal and so corrodes readily. This means that all steel objects that are to be used where moisture is present must be protected in some way. Mild steel is also naturally quite easily bent, which is an advantage for making shapes but a problem when using steel in vehicle panels. To overcome this problem the steel needs to be hardened.

▼ Despite being constantly exposed to moisture, all ships and most containers, are still made from steel. This is because the cost of using other materials would be vastly greater. As with most uses of steel, manufacturers have to compromise between resistance to corrosion and cost. As a result, much research goes into protective coatings. Many steel structures are also protected electrochemically by cathodic protection.

▼ Steel is widely used in the construction industry, for example, in reinforced concrete buildings. Here the strength of the steel helps to support the concrete. The steel mesh and rods used do not corrode, because once the concrete has set around them, the steel is protected from the air, and this prevents chemical corrosion.

▼ Steel will take a cutting edge well and is the main material used for making chisels, saw blades, twist drills and many other tools. Because it is not as hard as some other forms of steel, cutting tools will, however, require frequent sharpening.

► One of the major steel uses in the 19th century was railway lines: one quarter of a million miles of track were laid at this time.

▼ Steel is used as the body panels of almost all vehicles. It is a strong material, especially when formed into complex shapes, and it is relatively inexpensive. It can be formed into shapes when cold.

cathodic protection: the technique of making the object that is to be protected from corrosion into the cathode of a cell. For example, a material, such as steel, is protected by coupling it with a more reactive metal, such as magnesium. Steel forms the cathode and magnesium the anode. Zinc protects steel in the same way.

Hardening mild steel

Mild steel is relatively soft, and for many purposes it must be hardened. In steel the hardness depends on the amount of carbon present. Carbon becomes part of the structure of steel, making an alloy of iron and carbon atoms. The structure of the atoms can be layered and the properties changed by heating the steel in molten sodium cyanide. This makes the steel absorb nitrogen and carbon atoms, which, when the steel is cooled quickly, causes the surface to harden greatly. This is known as case hardening.

Steel can also be hardened by tempering. This is the process of reheating the steel and then cooling it without bringing about any chemical change. This process also makes the steel tougher and less liable to crack.

Special steels

Steel is an extremely versatile material whose properties can be tailored to a wide range of needs. For example, by changing the amount of carbon in the steel, the strength can be improved. In general the higher the carbon content, the tougher the steel. Thus, ordinary (mild) steel (described on page 32) contains 0.25% carbon; medium steels contain 0.5% carbon and high-carbon steels (the toughest) contain from 0.6% to 2% carbon. Varying the chemical content in this way is quite different from heating the metal and then cooling it quickly (quenching), a process that hardens the steel (see the previous page).

The reason that not all steels have a high carbon content is that it makes the steel more brittle. This is why mild steel is often preferred, for example, for pressing vehicle panels. But medium steels are best for beams and other construction uses, and high-carbon steels are preferred for machine tools.

Adding other metals to a steel also causes it to become harder. Manganese and silicon are two of the most commonly used alloying metals. Tungsten is an important alloying metal when hardness needs to be maintained even at very high temperatures, such as at the tip of a high-speed drill cutting into metal. Chromium and nickel as alloying elements are used to improve corrosion resistance, producing stainless steels. Silicon steel can be magnetized. Cobalt has a similar effect and is used to make permanent magnets. Finally, molybdenum and vanadium are also used as alloying metals for special steels.

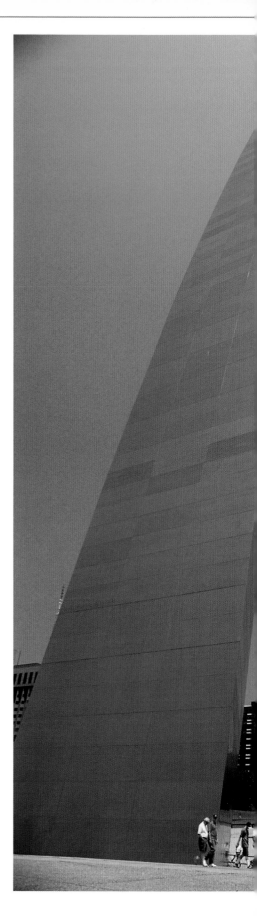

alloy: a mixture of a metal and various other elements.

◀ Gateway Arch, St. Louis, Missouri, designed by Eero Saarinen, is a monument to siding made from stainless steel. It is 192m high and took nearly two years to build.

Stainless steel

Stainless steels are a range of alloys based on iron. The name comes from the property of such steel to resist reactions with many other substances that may cause surface staining and rusting.

The most common stainless steels are iron-based alloys with a very high resistance to rusting and corrosion. This is because of their chromium content, which is greater than that found in other types of steel.

The most common stainless steel is made with 18% chromium, 8% nickel and 0.15% carbon. This is the type of stainless steel used for making everyday items such as cutlery.

▼ Stainless steel cutlery.

▲ Saws need to remain sharp for as long as possible. Many of the best-wearing blades are made from tungsten steel. The tungsten makes the steel considerably harder, and it is used in, for example, hard-wearing drills.

Chromium

Chromium, named after "chroma," the Greek word for color, was called this because of the many colored compounds that it makes. Among these are the rich red of rubies and the brilliant green of emeralds.

The main ore of chromium is chromite, found in combination with some iron ores.

Chromium ore is refined into shiny, silvery-white chromium metal. However, because chromium metal is brittle and hard, it has no uses on its own.

Chrome alloys
Chromium is used as an alloy with steel. Chrome steels are strong and hard and are often used for making tools. Chromium is always a component of stainless steel.

Alloys of nickel and chromium are used for high-temperature wire elements in electric heaters and other appliances.

▼ A piece of highly reflective chromium metal.

Chrome plating
Because chromium resists corrosion, is hard-wearing and has an attractive silvery color that does not tarnish, it is widely used to plate iron and brass.

All items to be chrome plated are dipped in a bath containing chromium compounds in solution. In some cases, the articles to be plated are simply dipped in chromium metal. But a thin, even finish is created by using the process of electrolysis. In this case the articles to be plated are attached to the negative end of an electrical circuit, and the surface is then plated.

Corrosion inhibitors
Because chromium compounds resist corrosion, they can be used as corrosion inhibitors in water-cooling systems, such as that of a motor vehicle.

alloy: a mixture of a metal and various other elements.

electrolysis: an electrical-chemical process that uses an electric current to cause the breakup of a compound and the movement of metal ions in a solution. The process happens in many natural situations (as for example in rusting) and is also commonly used in industry for purifying (refining) metals or for plating metal objects with a fine, even metal coating.

electroplating: depositing a thin layer of a metal onto the surface of another substance using electrolysis.

◀ Chrome was used as a decorative finish in many of the world's older classic cars. This is because, at the time, no other corrosion-resistant finish was available. Modern bumpers are not made of iron but of polycarbonate, and so do not need to be chromium protected at all.

Preparation of chromic acid

Chromic acid is prepared by stirring brown chromic oxide in water. The resulting acid is very corrosive and is used for cleaning glassware. It is also a strong oxidizing agent.

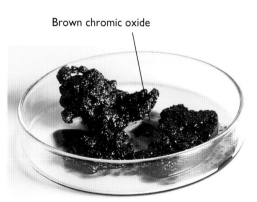

Brown chromic oxide

Brown chromic oxide is added to water

Chromic acid

EQUATION: Laboratory production of chromic acid

Chromic oxide + water ⇨ chromic acid

$$CrO_3(s) + H_2O(l) \Rightarrow H_2CrO_4(aq)$$

Chromium colors

Chromium compounds are mainly brightly colored. As a result, they are widely used as the coloring agent, or pigment, in paints, glazes, glass and enamels.

The most common colors for chromium compounds are green, yellow and orange.

Glaze

An important use of colored chrome oxide is to color glaze. A glaze is a mixture of coloring powder and powdered glass in water. The article to be glazed is then dipped in the mixture, or it may be sprayed on or brushed on.

The article is then fired so that the glass melts and forms a surface glaze.

Also...

Paint manufacturers are among the main users of chromium compounds. A paint must protect the surface to which it is applied and also provide a pleasing and decorative color. It must be easy to apply, make a thin even coating, and then dry quickly and uniformly.

Every paint is made of two parts, a powder of solid particles that gives the color and also makes the paint opaque. This is known as the pigment. The pigment is mixed into a liquid, called the binder, that allows the pigment to be spread evenly over the surface.

In some cases the binder is made from a solvent such as those based on petroleum. When applied, this evaporates and leaves a deposit of the pigment on the surface. At the same time, the binder reacts with oxygen of the air, becoming a nonsticky solid.

In many more cases, modern paints are being made with a water base for environmental reasons. However, pigments like chromium compounds do not easily mix with water and must be added already wrapped in their binder. This suspension of particles is called an emulsion.

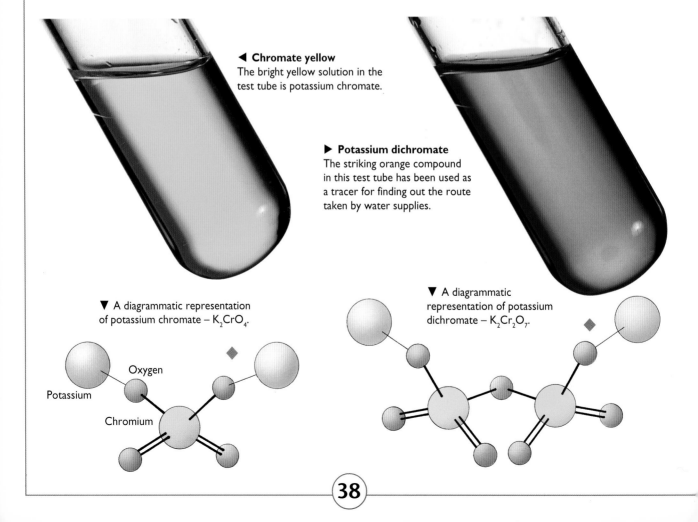

◀ **Chromate yellow**
The bright yellow solution in the test tube is potassium chromate.

▶ **Potassium dichromate**
The striking orange compound in this test tube has been used as a tracer for finding out the route taken by water supplies.

▼ A diagrammatic representation of potassium chromate – K_2CrO_4.

Potassium
Oxygen
Chromium

▼ A diagrammatic representation of potassium dichromate – $K_2Cr_2O_7$.

▶ Chromium III oxide
This green substance is
used as a pigment for paint.

▼ This is a yellow precipitate of lead chromate. It was prepared
by adding yellow potassium chromate solution to colorless lead
nitrate solution. The beaker is sitting on a magnetic stirrer that
spins the plastic coated metal mixer (sometimes called a "magnetic
flea") in the bottom. This thoroughly stirs the chemicals.
In this case the potassium chromate solution was added about
a second before the picture was taken.

Beaker

Solution of
lead nitrate

As soon as the
solution of potassium
chromate is added,
it is mixed with the
solution of lead
nitrate and forms
a yellow precipitate
of lead chromate.

Magnetic flea

Motor driving
the magnet

EQUATION: Reaction of potassium chromate and lead nitrate

Potassium chromate + lead II nitrate ⇨ lead chromate + potassium nitrate

$$K_2CrO_4(aq) \quad + \quad Pb(NO_3)_2(aq) \quad ⇨ \quad PbCrO_4(s) \quad + \quad 2KNO_3(aq)$$

Manganese

Manganese is a gray metal that looks very much like iron. Pure manganese is rarely used because it is hard and brittle. Its main use is as an alloying and purifying metal in the iron and steel industry.

Manganese is more reactive than iron (it is higher up the reactivity series), so when it is added to a furnace, the iron oxides react with the manganese, removing the oxygen from the iron and adding it to the manganese. Manganese oxide is one of the constituents of slag.

Manganese also reacts with sulfur impurities to form manganese sulfide, which then adds to the slag.

Manganese can be added to purified iron to make an alloy. The alloy is tougher, yet easier to work into shape than pure steel. It also gives added corrosion resistance. Manganese steel contains just over one-tenth manganese.

The alloy has the added advantage of being nonmagnetic. Its toughness means that it is used for the buckets and scoops of heavy lifting machinery and many other jobs in the construction industry.

When manganese makes the main component of an alloy with nonferrous metals like copper, it produces metals that expand and contract readily with temperature. As a result they are used in bimetal strips as heat-sensitive switches.

▲ A Venetian glass vase colored using compounds of manganese.

Manganese oxide in glassmaking

The Venetians were the first people to use manganese compounds in glassmaking. In the Middle Ages they discovered that manganese oxide would oxidize the iron impurities in the glass that gave it a green or brown tint. The result was a much clearer, and therefore more popular, glass.

▼ Garnet is a silicate in which manganese and iron are often important constituents, producing dark red-brown crystals. Garnet is widely regarded as a semiprecious stone.

EQUATION: Using manganese to help refine iron

Iron oxide + manganese ⇨ manganese oxide + iron

$$Fe_2O_3(s) \quad + \quad Mn(s) \quad ⇨ \quad MnO_3(s) \quad + \quad 2Fe(s)$$

Carbon rod cathode

Manganese oxide (MnO$_2$), carbon black and ammonium chloride (NH$_4$Cl)

◀ A dry cell.

Zinc cup, anode

Manganese oxide in batteries

Manganese oxide is the most commonly used compound of manganese. Under the name of pyrolusite, manganese oxide (a black powder) is bound in with the carbon electrodes of a dry battery.

Manganese oxide "traps" hydrogen gas that is given off as the chemicals of the battery react. In this way the dry battery does not swell up and burst from the formation of hydrogen gas.

The reactivity of manganese

Metals can be arranged in a reactivity series, with the most reactive at the top and the least reactive at the bottom. As you can see, manganese comes above iron in the list and so is more reactive. This means that manganese will remove the oxygen from iron in a heated furnace.

Manganese nodules

Manganese nodules are some of the richest concentrations of any element. The nodules contain mainly manganese and iron oxides, with some other metals such as cobalt and nickel.

The manganese nodules form naturally from metal compounds contained in materials sinking down through seawaters. Near the sea floor the manganese precipitates out of the seawater as small grains. These grains slowly attract more manganese compounds and eventually grow into nodules. At least half the mass of a manganese nodule is made of manganese.

Manganese nodules are found exclusively on the ocean floor, often lying scattered in huge fields. Each nodule can be the size of a golf ball.

REACTIVITY SERIES	
Element	*Reactivity*
potassium	*most reactive*
sodium	
calcium	
magnesium	
aluminum	
manganese	
chromium	
zinc	
iron	
cadmium	
tin	
lead	
copper	
mercury	
silver	
gold	
platinum	*least reactive*

Potassium permanganate

Manganese has compounds with striking colors. Some are used in the paint industry as pigments. Manganese sulfate is bright red and is used to color enamels; manganese carbonate is white.

When a manganese compound reacts with potassium nitrate, a deep green compound (potassium manganate) results. Further reaction with sulfuric acid produces purple potassium permanganate (an oxidizing agent used for bleaching and as a mild disinfectant).

▼ Potassium permanganate being used to investigate convection effects in a school laboratory tank.

◀ One of the most widely used compounds of manganese is potassium permanganate. It is a mild disinfectant. It is water-soluble and has a strong color, making it suitable for use as a tracing dye.

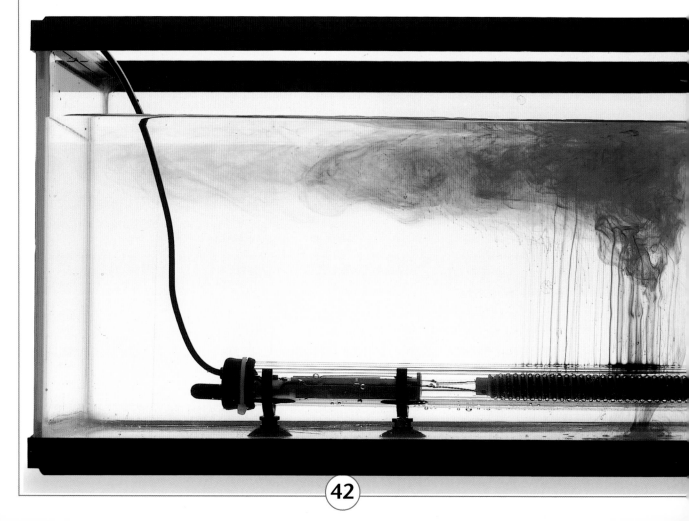

▼ Manganese oxide, potassium nitrate and potassium hydroxide at the start of the demonstration.

Potassium nitrate powder

Potassium hydroxide pellet

Black manganese oxide

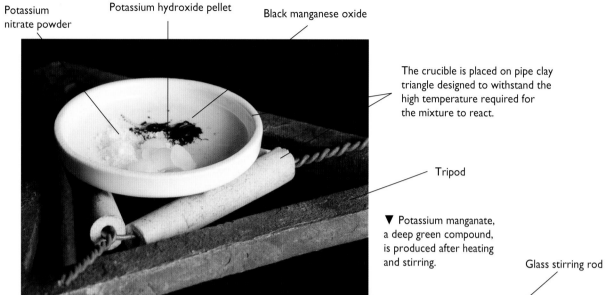

The crucible is placed on pipe clay triangle designed to withstand the high temperature required for the mixture to react.

Tripod

▼ Potassium manganate, a deep green compound, is produced after heating and stirring.

Glass stirring rod

Bunsen burner used to supply heat

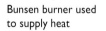

The preparation of potassium permanganate

Black manganese oxide powder is mixed with potassium nitrate and pellets of solid potassium hydroxide. Heated and stirred, they produce potassium manganate. When acidified and dried, this produces potassium permanganate.

The Periodic Table

Actinium (Ac)	89	
Aluminum (Al)	13	
Antimony (Sb)	51	
Americium (Am)	95	
Argon (Ar)	18	
Arsenic (As)	33	
Astatine (At)	85	
Barium (Ba)	56	
Berkelium (Bk)	97	
Beryllium (Be)	4	
Bismuth (Bi)	83	
Bohrium (Bh)	107	
Boron (B)	5	
Bromine (Br)	35	
Cadmium (Cd)	48	

Calcium (Ca)	20
Californium (Cf)	98
Carbon (C)	6
Cerium (Ce)	58
Cesium (Cs)	55
Chlorine (Cl)	17
Chromium (Cr)	24
Cobalt (Co)	27
Copper (Cu)	29
Curium (Cm)	96
Dubnium (Db)	105
Dysprosium (Dy)	66
Einsteinium (Es)	99
Erbium (Er)	68
Europium (Eu)	63

Fermium (Fm)	100
Fluorine (F)	9
Francium (Fr)	87
Gadolinium (Gd)	64
Gallium (Ga)	31
Germanium (Ge)	32
Gold (Au)	79
Hafnium (Hf)	72
Hassium (Hs)	108
Helium (He)	2
Holmium (Ho)	67
Hydrogen (H)	1
Indium (In)	49
Iodine (I)	53
Iridium (Ir)	77

GROUPS ▶

PERIODS ▼

Transition metals

Group	1 (1)	2 (2)	(3)	(4)	(5)	(6)	(7)	(8)
Period 1	1 H Hydrogen 1							
Period 2	3 Li Lithium 7	4 Be Beryllium 9						
Period 3	11 Na Sodium 23	12 Mg Magnesium 24						
Period 4	19 K Potassium 39	20 Ca Calcium 40	21 Sc Scandium 45	22 Ti Titanium 48	23 V Vanadium 51	24 Cr Chromium 52	25 Mn Manganese 55	26 Fe Iron 56
Period 5	37 Rb Rubidium 85	38 Sr Strontium 88	39 Y Yttrium 89	40 Zr Zirconium 91	41 Nb Niobium 93	42 Mo Molybdenum 96	43 Tc Technetium (99)	44 Ru Ruthenium 101
Period 6	55 Cs Cesium 133	56 Ba Barium 137	71 Lu Lutetium 175	72 Hf Hafnium 178	73 Ta Tantalum 181	74 W Tungsten 184	75 Re Rhenium 186	76 Os Osmium 190
Period 7	87 Fr Francium (223)	88 Ra Radium (226)	103 Lr Lawrencium (260)	104 Rf Rutherfordium (261)	105 Db Dubnium (262)	106 Sg Seaborgium (263)	107 Bh Bohrium (262)	108 Hs Hassium (265)

- ☐ Metals
- ☐ Metalloids (semimetals)
- ☐ Nonmetals
- ☐ Inner transition metals

Lanthanide series

57 La Lanthanum 139	58 Ce Cerium 140	59 Pr Praseodymium 141	60 Nd Neodymium 144

Actinide series

89 Ac Actinium (227)	90 Th Thorium (232)	91 Pa Protactinium (231)	92 U Uranium (238)

Iron (Fe) 26	Neptunium (Np) 93	Protactinium (Pa) 91	Strontium (Sr) 38	Ununoctium (Uuo) 118
Krypton (Kr) 36	Nickel (Ni) 28	Radium (Ra) 88	Sulfur (S) 16	Ununquadium (Uuq) 114
Lanthanum (La) 57	Niobium (Nb) 41	Radon (Rn) 86	Tantalum (Ta) 73	Unununium (Uuu) 111
Lawrencium (Lr) 103	Nitrogen (N) 7	Rhenium (Re) 75	Technetium (Tc) 43	Uranium (U) 92
Lead (Pb) 82	Nobelium (No) 102	Rhodium (Rh) 45	Tellurium (Te) 52	Vanadium (V) 23
Lithium (Li) 3	Osmium (Os) 76	Rubidium (Rb) 37	Terbium (Tb) 65	Xenon (Xe) 54
Lutetium (Lu) 71	Oxygen (O) 8	Ruthenium (Ru) 44	Thallium (Tl) 81	Ytterbium (Yb) 70
Magnesium (Mg) 12	Palladium (Pd) 46	Rutherfordium (Rf) 104	Thorium (Th) 90	Yttrium (Y) 39
Manganese (Mn) 25	Phosphorus (P) 15	Samarium (Sm) 62	Thulium (Tm) 69	Zinc (Zn) 30
Meitnerium (Mt) 109	Platinum (Pt) 78	Scandium (Sc) 21	Tin (Sn) 50	Zirconium (Zr) 40
Mendelevium (Md) 101	Plutonium (Pu) 94	Seaborgium (Sg) 106	Titanium (Ti) 22	
Mercury (Hg) 80	Polonium (Po) 84	Selenium (Se) 34	Tungsten (W) 74	
Molybdenum (Mo) 42	Potassium (K) 19	Silicon (Si) 14	Ununbium (Uub) 112	
Neodymium (Nd) 60	Praseodymium (Pr) 59	Silver (Ag) 47	Ununhexium (Uuh) 116	
Neon (Ne) 10	Promethium (Pm) 61	Sodium (Na) 11	Ununnilium (Uun) 110	

(9)	(10)	(11)	(12)	3 (13)	4 (14)	5 (15)	6 (16)	7 (17)	8 or 0 (18)
									2 **He** Helium 4
				5 **B** Boron 11	6 **C** Carbon 12	7 **N** Nitrogen 14	8 **O** Oxygen 16	9 **F** Fluorine 19	10 **Ne** Neon 20
				13 **Al** Aluminum 27	14 **Si** Silicon 28	15 **P** Phosphorus 31	16 **S** Sulfur 32	17 **Cl** Chlorine 35	18 **Ar** Argon 40
27 **Co** Cobalt 59	28 **Ni** Nickel 59	29 **Cu** Copper 64	30 **Zn** Zinc 65	31 **Ga** Gallium 70	32 **Ge** Germanium 73	33 **As** Arsenic 75	34 **Se** Selenium 79	35 **Br** Bromine 80	36 **Kr** Krypton 84
45 **Rh** Rhodium 103	46 **Pd** Palladium 106	47 **Ag** Silver 108	48 **Cd** Cadmium 112	49 **In** Indium 115	50 **Sn** Tin 119	51 **Sb** Antimony 122	52 **Te** Tellurium 128	53 **I** Iodine 127	54 **Xe** Xenon 131
77 **Ir** Iridium 192	78 **Pt** Platinum 195	79 **Au** Gold 197	80 **Hg** Mercury 201	81 **Tl** Thallium 204	82 **Pb** Lead 207	83 **Bi** Bismuth 209	84 **Po** Polonium (209)	85 **At** Astatine (210)	86 **Rn** Radon (222)
109 **Mt** Meitnerium (266)	110 **Uun** Unnnnilium (272)	111 **Uuu** Unununium (272)	112 **Uub** Ununbium (277)		114 **Uuq** Ununquadium (289)		116 **Uuh** Ununhexium (289)		118 **Uuo** Ununoctium (293)

61 **Pm** Promethium (145)	62 **Sm** Samarium 150	63 **Eu** Europium 152	64 **Gd** Gadolinium 157	65 **Tb** Terbium 159	66 **Dy** Dysprosium 163	67 **Ho** Holmium 165	68 **Er** Erbium 167	69 **Tm** Thulium 169	70 **Yb** Ytterbium 173
93 **Np** Neptunium (237)	94 **Pu** Plutonium (244)	95 **Am** Americium (243)	96 **Cm** Curium (247)	97 **Bk** Berkelium (247)	98 **Cf** Californium (251)	99 **Es** Einsteinium (252)	100 **Fm** Fermium (257)	101 **Md** Mendelevium (258)	102 **No** Nobelium (259)

45

Understanding equations

As you read through Volumes 1 to 15 in the Elements set, you will notice that many pages contain equations using symbols. Symbols make it easy for chemists to write out the reactions that are occurring in a way that allows a better understanding of the processes involved. If you are not familiar with these symbols, these pages explain them.

Symbols for the elements

The basis for the modern use of symbols for elements dates back to the 19th century. At that time a shorthand was developed using the first letter of the element wherever possible.

Thus O stands for oxygen, H stands for hydrogen, and so on. However, if we were to use only the first letter, there could be some confusion. For example, nitrogen and nickel would both use the symbols N. To overcome this problem, many element symbols take the first two letters of the full name, with the second letter in lowercase. So, although nitrogen is N, nickel becomes Ni. Not all symbols come from the English name; many use the Latin name instead. That is why, for example, gold is not G but Au (from the Latin *aurum*), and sodium has the symbol Na (from the Latin *natrium*).

Compounds of elements are made by combining letters. So, the molecule carbon

Written and symbolic equations

In this book important chemical equations are briefly stated in words (they are called word equations) and are then shown in their symbolic form along with the states.

What reaction the equation illustrates

EQUATION: The formation of calcium hydroxide

Word equation ——— *Calcium oxide + water ⇨ calcium hydroxide*

Symbol equation ——— $CaO(s)$ + $H_2O(l)$ ⇨ $Ca(OH)_2(aq)$

heated

Sometimes you will find additional descriptions below the symbolic equation.

Symbol showing the state: *s* is for solid, *l* is for liquid, *g* is for gas, and *aq* is for aqueous.

Diagrams

Some of the equations are shown as graphic representations.

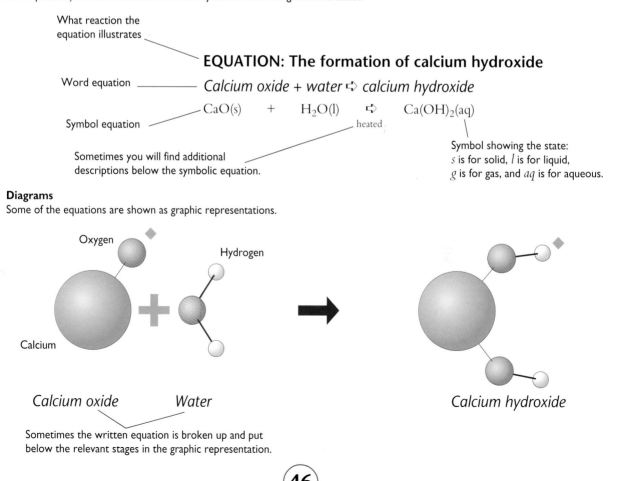

Oxygen

Hydrogen

Calcium

Calcium oxide   *Water*

Calcium hydroxide

Sometimes the written equation is broken up and put below the relevant stages in the graphic representation.

monoxide is CO. By using lowercase letters for the second letter of an element, it is possible to show that cobalt, symbol Co, is not the same as the molecule carbon monoxide, CO.

However, the letters can be made to do much more than this. In many molecules atoms combine in unequal numbers. So, for example, carbon dioxide has one atom of carbon for every two of oxygen. That is shown by using the number 2 beside the oxygen, and the symbol becomes CO_2.

In practice some groups of atoms combine as a unit with other substances. Thus, for example, calcium bicarbonate (one of the compounds used in some antacid pills) is written $Ca(HCO_3)_2$. This shows that the part of the substance inside the parentheses reacts as a unit, and the 2 outside the parentheses shows the presence of two such units.

Some substances attract water molecules to themselves. To show this, a dot is used. So, the blue form of copper sulfate is written $CuSO_4.5H_2O$. In this case five molecules of water attract to one of copper sulfate. When you see the dot, you know that this water can be driven off by heating; it is part of the crystal structure.

In a reaction substances change by rearranging the combinations of atoms. The way they change is shown by using the chemical symbols, placing those that will react (the starting materials, or reactants) on the left and the products of the reaction on the right. Between the two an arrow shows which way the reaction is going.

It is possible to describe a reaction in words. That produces word equations, which are given throughout Volumes 1 to 15. However, it is easier to understand what is happening by using an equation containing symbols. They are also given in many places. They are not shown when the equations are very complex.

In any equation both sides balance; that is, there must be an equal number of like atoms on both sides of the arrow. When you try to write down reactions, you, too, must balance your equation; you cannot have a few atoms left over at the end!

The symbols in parentheses are abbreviations for the physical state of each substance taking part, so that (s) is used for solid, (l) for liquid, (g) for gas, and (aq) for an aqueous solution, that is, a solution of a substance dissolved in water.

Atoms and ions
Each sphere represents a particle of an element. A particle can be an atom or an ion. Each atom or ion is associated with other atoms or ions through bonds – forces of attraction. The size of the particles and the nature of the bonds can be extremely important in determining the nature of the reaction or the properties of the compound.

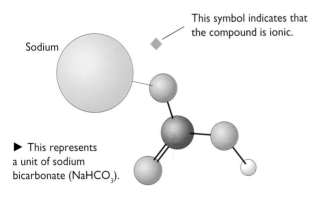

Sodium

This symbol indicates that the compound is ionic.

▶ This represents a unit of sodium bicarbonate ($NaHCO_3$).

The term "unit" is sometimes used to simplify the representation of a combination of ions.

Chemical symbols, equations, and diagrams
The arrangement of any molecule or compound can be shown in one of the two ways shown below, depending on which gives the clearer picture. The left-hand image is called a ball-and-stick diagram because it uses rods and spheres to show the structure of the material. This example shows water, H_2O. There are two hydrogen atoms and one oxygen atom.

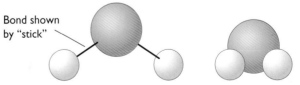

Bond shown by "stick"

Colors too
The colors of each of the particles help differentiate the elements involved. The diagram can then be matched to the written and symbolic equation given with the diagram. In the case above, oxygen is red, and hydrogen is gray.

Key facts about...

Name: iron
Symbol: Fe
Atomic number: 26
Atomic weight: 55.84
Position in Periodic Table: transition metal, group (8) (iron group); period 4
State at room temperature: solid
Color: steel-gray
Origin of name: from the Anglo-Saxon word *iren*. The symbol Fe comes from the Latin word *ferrum*, meaning iron.
Shell pattern of electrons: 2–8–14–2
Further facts on this element can be found in Volume 17: Francium to Polonium

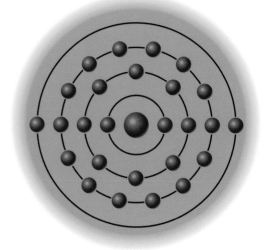

Name: chromium
Symbol: Cr
Atomic number: 24
Atomic weight: 51.99
Position in Periodic Table: transition metal, group (6) (chromium group); period 4
State at room temperature: solid
Color: steel-gray
Origin of name: from the Greek word *chroma*, meaning color, a reflection of the wide variety of colors found in chromium compounds.
Shell pattern of electrons: 2–8–13–1
Further facts on this element can be found in Volume 16: Actinium to Fluorine

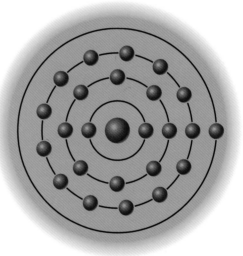

Name: manganese
Symbol: Mn
Atomic number: 25
Atomic weight: 54.94
Position in Periodic Table: transition metal, group (7) (manganese group); period 4
State at room temperature: solid
Color: silvery-white
Density of solid: 7.44 g/cc
Melting point: 1,246°C
Boiling point: 2,061°C
Origin of name: from the Latin word *magnes*, meaning magnet
Shell pattern of electrons: 2–8–13–2
Further facts on this element can be found in Volume 17: Francium to Polonium

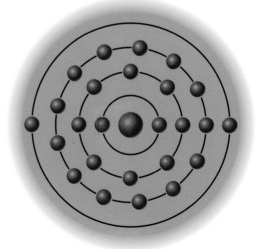

Glossary of technical terms

acidity: a general term for the strength of an acid in a solution.

alloy: a mixture of a metal and various other elements.

cathodic protection: the technique of making the object that is to be protected from corrosion into the cathode of a cell. For example, a material, such as steel, is protected by coupling it with a more reactive metal, such as magnesium. Steel forms the cathode and magnesium the anode. Zinc protects steel in the same way.

corrosion: the *slow* decay of a substance resulting from contact with gases and liquids in the environment. The term is often applied to metals. Rust is the corrosion of iron.

decompose: to break down a substance (for example, by heat or with the aid of a catalyst) into simpler components. In such a chemical reaction only one substance is involved.

electrode: a conductor that forms one terminal of a cell.

electrolysis: an electrical-chemical process that uses an electric current to cause the breakup of a compound and the movement of metal ions in a solution. The process happens in many natural situations (as for example in rusting) and is also commonly used in industry for purifying (refining) metals or for plating metal objects with a fine, even metal coating.

electrolyte: a solution that conducts electricity.

electroplating: depositing a thin layer of a metal onto the surface of another substance using electrolysis.

gelatinous: a term meaning made with water. Because a gelatinous precipitate is mostly water, it is of a similar density to water and will float or lie suspended in the liquid.

ion: an atom, or group of atoms, that has gained or lost one or more electrons and so developed an electrical charge. Ions behave differently from electrically neutral atoms and molecules. They can move in an electric field, and they can also bind strongly to solvent molecules such as water. Positively charged ions are called cations; negatively charged ions are called anions. Ions carry electrical current through solutions.

native metal: a pure form of a metal, not combined as a compound. Native metal is more common in poorly reactive elements than in those that are very reactive.

ore: a rock containing enough of a useful substance to make mining it worthwhile.

oxidation: a reaction in which the oxidizing agent removes electrons. (Note that oxidizing agents do not have to contain oxygen.)

oxide: a compound that includes oxygen and one other element.

oxidizing agent: a substance that removes electrons from another substance (and therefore is itself reduced).

porous: a material containing many small holes or cracks. Quite often the pores are connected, and liquids, such as water or oil, can move through them.

precipitate: tiny solid particles formed as a result of a chemical reaction between two liquids or gases.

product: a substance produced by a chemical reaction.

pyrite: "mineral of fire". This name comes from the fact that pyrite (iron sulfide) will give off sparks if struck with a stone.

reactivity: the tendency of a substance to react with other substances. The term is most widely used in comparing the reactivity of metals. Metals are arranged in a reactivity series.

reduction: the removal of oxygen from a substance.

reducing agent: a substance that gives electrons to another substance. Carbon monoxide is a reducing agent when passed over copper oxide, turning it to copper and producing carbon dioxide gas. Similarly, iron oxide is reduced to iron in a blast furnace. Sulfur dioxide is a reducing agent used for bleaching bread.

solution: a mixture of a liquid and at least one other substance (e.g., saltwater). Mixtures can be separated by physical means, for example, by evaporation and cooling.

slag: a mixture of substances that are waste products of a furnace. Most slags are composed mainly of silicates.

sulfide: a sulfur compound that contains no oxygen.

Set Index

USING THE SET INDEX

The 18 volumes in the *Elements* set are:

Volume
Number   Title

1. Hydrogen and the Noble Gases
2. Sodium and Potassium
3. Calcium and Magnesium
4. Iron, Chromium, and Manganese
5. Copper, Silver, and Gold
6. Zinc, Cadmium, and Mercury
7. Aluminum
8. Carbon
9. Silicon
10. Lead and Tin
11. Nitrogen and Phosphorus
12. Oxygen
13. Sulfur
14. Chlorine, Fluorine, Bromine, and Iodine
15. Uranium and Other Radioactive Elements
16. Actinium to Fluorine
17. Francium to Polonium
18. Potassium to Zirconium

An example entry:

Index entries are listed alphabetically. Volume numbers are in bold and are followed by page references in roman.

sodium (Na) **See Vol. 2 and Vol. 18:** 24–25; **1:** 36, **7:** 6, **9:** 11, 24, 38

In this case sodium gets extensive coverage in Volume 2: Sodium and Potassium and on pages 24 and 25 of Volume 18: Potassium to Zirconium. Sodium is also discussed on page 36 of Volume 1, page 6 of Volume 7, and pages 11, 24, and 38 of Volume 9.

A

A-bomb **15:** 38
Ac *see* actinium
acetate **8:** 41
acetic acid **1:** 31, **7:** 33, **8:** 29
acetone **7:** 34, **8:** 28
acetylene **8:** 29, **14:** 22
acid **1:** 12, 18, 19, 20, 22, 23, 34, 35, 36, 37, **2:** 31, **3:** 12, 21, 29, 39, 42, **7:** 14, 33, **13:** 19, 26, 27
acid burn **1:** 24, **13:** 26, **2:** 32, 33, **3:** 13, **4:** 10, **7:** 40, 42, 43, **10:** 12, **11:** 31, 32, **12:** 13, 29, 42, **13:** 18, 19, 22, 23
acidity **1:** 20–21
acidosis **1:** 28
acids **9:** 11
acid soil **4:** 17
actinides, actinide series **16:** 8 *see also* Periodic Table
actinium (Ac) **16:** 17
activated charcoal **8:** 22, 23, **14:** 27

addition polymer **8:** 32–35
adhesive **3:** 22, 23, **12:** 20
admiralty brass **5:** 18
adsorption **14:** 27, **7:** 35, **8:** 23
aeration **12:** 8, 9
aeroembolism **11:** 7
Ag *see* silver
agate **9:** 13, 14
Agent Orange **14:** 29
air **11:** 38, **12:** 6, 7, 17
air bag **11:** 29
Al *see* aluminum
alchemists, alchemy **1:** 22, 23, **15:** 11
alclad **7:** 23
alcohols **8:** 28
algae **3:** 4, 40, **11:** 43
algal blooms **11:** 43
alkali **1:** 20, 34, 35, **2:** 5, 32, **7:** 14, 33, 36, **11:** 12, 14, 15, 39
alkaline **1:** 20, 32, 33, **2:** 6, 31, 32
alkanes (paraffins) **8:** 28
alloy **4:** 34, 35, 36–37, 40, **5:** 20, **6:** 20, 22, 41, **7:** 22–23, **9:** 31, **10:** 40, 41
alpha particle **15:** 8, 42
alpha radiation **15:** 8, 9
alum **7:** 4, 7, 36, **8:** 15
alumina **7:** 16, 17, 18, 19, 34
alumina–silica gel **8:** 27, **1:** 26, 36
aluminum (Al) **See Vol. 7 and Vol. 16:** 18–19; **1:** 26, 36, **2:** 32, **4:** 22, 23, **5:** 21, 35, **6:** 22, **9:** 11, 20, 26, 34, 37, **10:** 39, **11:** 37, **12:** 10, 38, **15:** 9
aluminum foil **7:** 21, 30
aluminum hydroxide **7:** 36, 37, 38
aluminum oxide **7:** 7, 14, 16, 17, 18, 34, 35, **8:** 20, 21, **9:** 13, **12:** 11, 39, **4:** 17
aluminum silicate **9:** 26
aluminum sulfate **7:** 7, 36, 38, **8:** 15
Am *see* americium
amalgam **5:** 35, 42, **6:** 26, 36, 37, **7:** 22, **14:** 19
amalgamation **5:** 39
Amatol **11:** 27
americium (Am) **16:** 21
amethyst **9:** 12
amino acids **8:** 36
ammonia **1:** 16–17, 22, 26, 27, 32, **2:** 28, 29, **7:** 36, **11:** 12–17, 36, 37, **13:** 36, 43, **14:** 17, 34, 39
ammonia fountain **11:** 15
ammonia solution **5:** 27
ammonite **3:** 9
ammonium chloride **1:** 22, 23, **2:** 28, 29, **4:** 41, **6:** 14, 15, **11:** 13, 14, 34
ammonium dichromate **11:** 24, 25
ammonium hydroxide **11:** 12
ammonium nitrate **11:** 13, 27
ammonium nitrite **11:** 27
ammonium perchlorate **12:** 39, **14:** 24
ammonium sulfate **7:** 36, **11:** 14, **13:** 43

ammunition **10:** 15, **11:** 27
amorphous **9:** 38
amphiboles **9:** 24
amphoteric **6:** 10, **7:** 14
anesthetics **14:** 5
anglesite **10:** 7
anhydrous **13:** 34
anions **3:** 29, **6:** 12,
annealing **7:** 20, **9:** 41
anode **2:** 23, 26, **3:** 37, **6:** 12, 13, **7:** 19, 25, **10:** 11
anodizing **7:** 26
antacid **2:** 31, **3:** 5, 42, 47, **8:** 15
anthracite **8:** 7
antibacterial agent **6:** 38
antimony (Sb) **See Vol. 16:** 20; **10:** 15, 40
antimony-133 **15:** 29
antioxidant **11:** 10
antiseptic **14:** 41
apatite **11:** 42
approximate relative atomic mass **16:** 7
aqua fortis **1:** 26, **11:** 36
aqua regia **1:** 22, 26, **5:** 41, **11:** 36
aquamarine **9:** 23, **12:** 10
aquifers **2:** 20
architectural brass **5:** 19
Ar *see* argon
argon (Ar) **See Vol. 1 and Vol. 16:** 22; **4:** 30, **11:** 8, 9, **12:** 17, **15:** 11
arsenic (As) **See Vol. 16:** 23; **2:** 30, **13:** 42
As *see* arsenic
asbestos **14:** 20
asphalt **8:** 26, 27
aspirin **1:** 30
astatine (At) **16:** 24
At *see* astatine
atmosphere **3:** 12, **11:** 6, **12:** 6, 8, 12
atom, atoms **1–15:** 47, **16–18:** 57; **1:** 4, 38, **8:** 8, **15:** 4, 7, **16:** 4, 11
atomic bomb **15:** 38, 39
atomic mass **16:** 15 *see also* approximate relative atomic mass
atomic number **16:** 4, 7, 15
atomic weight **16:** 15
Au *see* gold
augite **9:** 24
aurora **12:** 7, **11:** 7
Australia **7:** 11
azide **11:** 29

B

B *see* boron
Ba *see* barium
background radiation **15:** 14–15
Bacon, Roger **11:** 26
bacteria **13:** 8, 20
Baekland, Leo **8:** 31
Bakelite **8:** 31
baking powder **2:** 30
baking soda **2:** 28, 30, **8:** 14
barite **13:** 12, **16:** 24, 25
barium (Ba) **16:** 25
barium chlorate **14:** 24
barium-142 **15:** 28
barium peroxide **4:** 22
barium sulfate **13:** 12
barometer **6:** 30

basalt **9:** 24, 43, **15:** 18
base **1:** 22, 23, 32–33, 34, **2:** 32, **3:** 21, 25
base bullion **10:** 10
basic-oxygen furnace process **4:** 30, 31
basic-oxygen process **12:** 27
battery **4:** 41, **6:** 5, 12, **10:** 28, **13:** 30, 31
bauxite **7:** 10–11, 13, 14, 16, 18
Bayer, Karl Joseph **7:** 12
Bayer process **7:** 14, 16
Be *see* beryllium
becquerel **15:** 13, 22
Becquerel, A. H. **6:** 35, **15:** 5, 12, 22
bell-making bronze **5:** 21
bends **11:** 7
Benin bronze **5:** 19
benzene ring **8:** 33
berkelium (Bk) **16:** 26
beryl **7:** 8, **9:** 22
beryllium (Be) **See Vol. 16:** 27; **7:** 8, **9:** 22
Bessemer Converter **4:** 31, **12:** 27
Bessemer, Sir Henry **4:** 31
beta particle **15:** 8
beta radiation **15:** 8, 9
Bh *see* bohrium
Bi *see* bismuth
bicarbonate **1:** 29, 31
Big Bang **15:** 7
biotite **7:** 6, **9:** 26
bismuth (Bi) **See Vol. 16:** 28; **10:** 11
Bk *see* berkelium
black phosphorus **11:** 38
blast furnace **4:** 24, 25, 26, 27, **12:** 26
bleach **4:** 42, **12:** 21, **13:** 18, 20–21, **14:** 14, 15, 24
bleaching agent **13:** 18–21
blood **12:** 15
blood (salts) **2:** 18, 19
blue–green algae **11:** 18, 19, 22
Blue John **14:** 8, 36
blue vitriol **5:** 24, **13:** 32
body **2:** 18,19, **3:** 5, 32
bog iron ore **4:** 13
bohrium (Bh) **16:** 29
bond **1:** 9, 11, **2:** 23, **3:** 47
bone **3:** 5, 32
Bordeaux mixture **5:** 23, **13:** 34, 42
bornite **5:** 6
boron (B) **16:** 30
boron oxide **9:** 38
borosilicate glass **9:** 39, **16:** 30
Br *see* bromine
brass **5:** 18–19, 20, 27, **6:** 4, 20, **10:** 15
braze **5:** 18, **7:** 20
Brazil **7:** 11
breeder reactor **15:** 35
brimstone **13:** 4, 5, 10
brimstone and treacle **13:** 42
brine **1:** 14, 15, **2:** 12, 13, 25, 26, 27, 28, 29, 40, **6:** 33, **14:** 18, 19, 20
bromide **14:** 4
bromine (Br) **See Vol. 14 and Vol. 16:** 31; **8:** 23
bromothymol blue **1:** 21
bronze **5:** 20–21, 27, 34, **6:** 20, 21, **10:** 40, 41

Bronze Age **5:** 20, **10:** 5, 41
buckled ring **13:** 6
buckminsterfullerene **8:** 8, 22
buffer **1:** 28, 29
building stone **3:** 18
burette **1:** 35
burnt lime **3:** 22
burnt ocher **4:** 13
butane **8:** 7, 26, 28

C

C *see* carbon
Ca *see* calcium
cadmium (Cd) **See Vol. 6 and Vol. 16:** 32; **15:** 34
cadmium battery **6:** 41
cadmium borate **6:** 42
cadmium hydroxide **6:** 41
cadmium plating **6:** 40
cadmium sulfide **6:** 40, 42, 43, **9:** 41, **13:** 12, 24, 25
cadmium telluride **6:** 42
cadmium test **6:** 40
calcite **3:** 8, 10, 14, 16, 33, **9:** 18
calcium (Ca) **See Vol. 3 and Vol. 16:** 33–34; **7:** 6, **9:** 11, 20, 38
calcium bicarbonate **1:** 29, **3:** 15, 27, 38, 42
calcium carbonate **1:** 23, 29, 34, **3:** 4, 8, 12, 15, 16, 21, 26, 33, 39, 43, **4:** 31, **8:** 15, **9:** 9, 18, 39, 40, **14:** 35
calcium chlorate **14:** 14, 16, 24
calcium chloride **2:** 28, **14:** 19
calcium fluoride **3:** 8, **14:** 8, 9
calcium hydrogen carbonate **3:** 38
calcium hydroxide **3:** 6, 24, 26, 28, **11:** 14
calcium ions **3:** 25, 28, 40,
calcium oxide **2:** 29, **3:** 20, 24, 46, **4:** 26, 31, **7:** 16, **11:** 14, **12:** 26, **14:** 14
calcium phosphate **3:** 32, **11:** 38, 42, 43, **14:** 37
calcium silicate **4:** 26
calcium sulfate **3:** 8, 30, **4:** 25, **13:** 9, 12, 13, 32, **11:** 43
californium (Cf) **16:** 35
calomel **6:** 32
camphor **8:** 31
cancer **15:** 42
cans **7:** 32, 33, 40
carats **5:** 40
carbohydrate **8:** 18
carbon (C) **See Vol. 8 and Vol. 16:** 10, 13, 36–37; **1:** 24, **4:** 27, 28, 29, 30, 31, 32, 34, 41, **6:** 14, 15, **7:** 18, 19, **9:** 13, **10:** 8, 10, **12:** 24, 26, **13:** 26, 27, **14:** 13, 15, **15:** 7
carbon black **4:** 41, **8:** 22
carbon compounds **8:** 6
carbon cycle **8:** 10–11, 13
carbon dating **15:** 18
carbon dioxide **1:** 23, **2:** 28, 29, 30, 31, 32, **3:** 12, 19, 26, 43, 47, **4:** 26, 27, **7:** 38, 39, **8:** 10, 11, 12–15, 18, **11:** 8, **12:** 14, 15, 24, 38, 41
carbon dioxide, radioactive **15:** 14
carbon-14 **11:** 6, **15:** 7, 10, 16, 17, 19
carbonic acid **1:** 28–29, **3:** 12
Carboniferous Period **8:** 7

carbon monoxide **4:** 24, 27, 30, **5:** 8, 9, **6:** 8, **8:** 16–17, **10:** 8, **12:** 13, 24
carbon rod **4:** 41
carbon tetrachloride **14:** 30
carbon-12 **15:** 7
carbonyl compounds **8:** 28
carborundum **8:** 5
carboxylic acid **1:** 30
carnellian **9:** 13
case hardening **4:** 33
cassiterite **10:** 34
cast iron **4:** 24, 28, 29
casting **6:** 22, 23, **7:** 22
Castner, Hamilton **2:** 26
Castner–Kellner cell **6:** 33
Castner–Kellner process **14:** 18–19
catalyst **1:** 12, 13, 17, **8:** 27, **11:** 17, **13:** 22, 28
catalytic converter **12:** 41, **8:** 16, **10:** 33
cathode **2:** 23, 27, **3:** 37, **4:** 41, **6:** 12, 13, **7:** 18, 19, **10:** 11
cathode ray tube **6:** 42
cathodic protection **4:** 7, 32, 33, **12:** 32, 33
cathodic protector **7:** 25
cation **2:** 15, 35, **3:** 29
cat's-eye **9:** 13
caustic **3:** 22
caustic soda **1:** 32, **2:** 6, 32, 34, 35, **7:** 15
caves, cave formations and caverns **3:** 14
Cd *see* cadmium
Ce *see* cerium
cell **6:** 13
cellulose **8:** 18, 31, 38, **12:** 14
cellulose acetate **8:** 31
cellulose nitrate **8:** 31
cement **3:** 5, 21, 22, **9:** 18
ceramic **9:** 29, 31
cerise **10:** 30
cerium (Ce) **16:** 38
cerussite **10:** 7
cesium (Cs) **16:** 39
cesium-137 **15:** 39
Cf *see* californium
CFCs *see* chlorofluorocarbons
chain silicates **9:** 24
chalcedony **9:** 13
chalcopyrite **5:** 6, **13:** 12
chalk **3:** 4, 10
chalk **8:** 10
charcoal **8:** 22–23, **11:** 26, **13:** 41
charge, furnace **4:** 24, 25
chemical bonds **8:** 7
Chernobyl **15:** 37
china clay **9:** 26, 28
chlorates **14:** 24
chloride ions **1:** 34, **2:** 9, 22, 26, **14:** 8, 20
chlorinated hydrocarbons **14:** 30
chlorination **14:** 11
chlorine (Cl) **See Vol. 14 and Vol. 16:** 11, 14, 40–41; **1:** 15, **2:** 7, 12, 23, 26, 27, **6:** 33, **8:** 33, **12:** 12, **13:** 20, 40
chloroethylene **8:** 33, **14:** 23
chlorofluorocarbons **12:** 12, **14:** 38, 39
chloroform **14:** 5
chlorophyll **3:** 34

cholera **14:** 16
chromatography **7:** 35, **8:** 20
chrome **12:** 32
chrome alloys **4:** 36
chrome oxide **4:** 38
chrome steel **4:** 36
chromic acid **4:** 37
chromic oxide **4:** 37
chromite **4:** 36
chromium (Cr) **See Vol. 4 and Vol. 16:** 42; **9:** 29
chromium oxide **11:** 24, 25
chromium III oxide **4:** 39
cinnabar **6:** 5, 26
circuit **9:** 36, 37
citric acid **1:** 18, 30, 31
citrine **9:** 12
Cl *see* chlorine
clay **3:** 29, **7:** 7, 8, 34, 36, **9:** 26, 29
Cm *see* curium
CN gas **14:** 26
Co *see* cobalt
coal **8:** 7, 10, 13, **12:** 24, 38
cobalt (Co) **See Vol. 16:** 43; **4:** 34, 41, **9:** 7, 41
cobalt hydroxide **1:** 33
cobalt sulfide **13:** 24
cobalt-60 **15:** 17, 27, 43
coinage metals **5:** 4
coins **5:** 20, 28, 41
coke **1:** 24, **4:** 25, 27, **5:** 11, **10:** 10, **12:** 24, 26, 29, **13:** 27
collector **9:** 36
color **3:** 8, 10
combustion **11:** 39, **12:** 34, 38, **13:** 14
compounds **2:** 5, 22, **3:** 4, 7, 41, **4:** 20, **8:** 7, **11:** 39, 41, **12:** 15, 35, 39, **13:** 15, **16:** 4, 11–13
Comstock Lode **5:** 30, 31
concentrated acid **1:** 19
conchoidal fracture **9:** 15
concrete **3:** 5, 23, **15:** 9, 35
condensation nuclei **14:** 8, 40
condensation polymers **8:** 36–37
conduction, electrical **2:** 22, 23, **5:** 16, **7:** 28, **12:** 9
conduction, heat **5:** 15, **7:** 29, 30, 31
Contact process **13:** 28–29
control rods **15:** 34, 35
copper (Cu) **See Vol. 5 and Vol. 16:** 11, 44–45; **1:** 12, 29, **2:** 23, **4:** 6, 7, 40, **6:** 8, 10, 12, 20, 22, 37, **7:** 4, 22, 28, **8:** 17, **10:** 11, 15, 41, **11:** 5, 30, 37, **12:** 25, 28, 29, **14:** 12
copper carbonate **5:** 6, 7, 26, 27, **13:** 34
copper chlorate **14:** 24
copper chloride **14:** 12
copper complex **5:** 27, **13:** 37
copper deficiency **5:** 22
copper hydroxide **1:** 33, **5:** 27
copper nitrate **5:** 14, 26, **11:** 31
copper ores **5:** 6–7, 10
copper oxide **5:** 8, 9, 11, 24, 26, **8:** 17, **12:** 23, 25
copper sulfate **1:** 25, **3:** 37, **4:** 6, 7, **5:** 13, 23, 24, 26, **6:** 10, 12, **12:** 28, **13:** 32, 34–37, 42
copper sulfide **5:** 8, 11, 26, **12:** 29, **13:** 12, 13
coral **3:** 4, 9, 10

corrosion **1:** 9, 26, 36, **3:** 13, 36, **4:** 6, 7, 8, 9, 10, 32, 35, 37, 40, 41, **5:** 15, 21, **6:** 16, **7:** 14, 33, **10:** 38, **12:** 30, 32
corundum **7:** 6, 9, **12:** 11
cosmetics **10:** 30
cosmic radiation **15:** 10, 14, 15
covalent bond **1:** 11
Cr *see* chromium
cracking **1:** 14, 15, **8:** 26, 27
cross-linking **8:** 34
crude oil **1:** 14, 15, **8:** 24, 25, 26, 27
cryogenics **1:** 41
cryolite **7:** 18
crystal **2:** 8, 9, 13, 22, 35, **9:** 10, 11, 12, 13, 14, 15, 20, 21, 24, 25, 28, 29, 37
crystals **3:** 8, **4:** 13, **5:** 24, **7:** 6, 16, **8:** 8–9, **13:** 10–11, 33, **14:** 8
Cs *see* cesium
CS gas **14:** 26
Cu *see* copper
cubic **9:** 20
cubic crystal **2:** 8, 9, 22, **4:** 18, 19, **13:** 12, 13, 15
cubic zirconia **9:** 21
curie **15:** 13, 22
Curie, Marie and Pierre **15:** 5, 22, 23
curing **2:** 25
curium (Cm) **16:** 46
currency **5:** 41
current **9:** 34
cyanide **14:** 26
cyclotrimethylenetrinitramine **11:** 27
Czochralski method **9:** 35

D

Daniell cell **6:** 13
Daniell, John **6:** 12
Darby, Abraham **4:** 5
Db *see* dubnium
DDT **8:** 42, **14:** 29
decomposition **4:** 23, **10:** 20, 21, **11:** 25, 32, **14:** 7
decorative brass **5:** 19
decrepitation **11:** 32
deflagrating spoon **13:** 14
dehydrating agent **13:** 26
dehydration **1:** 24, **8:** 19
deionized **1:** 10
denitrifying bacteria **11:** 23
dental **14:** 5
desalination **2:** 14
desert roses **3:** 8, **13:** 13
detergent **2:** 37, 40, **3:** 40, **12:** 21, **11:** 43
deuterium **15:** 30, 38
deuterium-tritium fusion **15:** 30
dialysis **2:** 19
diamond **7:** 6, **8:** 8, **9:** 12, 13, 21, **14:** 37, **16:** 10
diaphragm (electrolysis) **2:** 26
diaphragm cell **1:** 14, **14:** 18, 20, 21, 25
dichlorodiethyl sulfide **13:** 40
die-casting **6:** 22
diesel **1:** 14, **8:** 26, 27
dilute acid **1:** 19
diode **9:** 34, 35, 37
dioxins **14:** 29

diphosphine **11:** 39
discharge tube **1:** 43, **2:** 38, 39
disinfectant **4:** 42, **11:** 12, **14:** 16, 43
displacement reaction **14:** 41
dissociate **1:** 11, 19, 30, 31, 32, **2:** 22
dissolve **2:** 25, **3:** 12
dissolving, aluminum **7:** 14–15
distillation **8:** 25
distilling nitrogen **11:** 8
DNA **1:** 8, 9
dolomite **3:** 5, 37, **10:** 7, **12:** 27
doping **9:** 35
Downs process **2:** 26, **14:** 19
dry ammonia **11:** 14
dry batteries (cell) **6:** 5, 14
dry cell **4:** 41
dry cleaning **14:** 30
dry ice **8:** 14
dry zinc–silver battery **6:** 13
dubnium (Db) **16:** 47
duralumin **7:** 23
Dy *see* dysprosium
dyes **1:** 24, **7:** 37
dynamite **11:** 13, 27, 28
dysprosium (Dy) **16:** 48

E

ebonite **13:** 38
einsteinium (Es) **16:** 49
ekaboron (Eb) *see* scandium
electrical cable **7:** 28
electrical conduction **2:** 23, 23
electrical conductor **5:** 16
electric arc process **4:** 30
electricity **9:** 34
electrode **3:** 37, **4:** 11, 41, **6:** 12, 13, **7:** 25
electrolysis **1:** 10, 11, 15, **2:** 23, 26–27, **4:** 11, 37, **5:** 12, 13, **6:** 9, **7:** 18, 19, **12:** 28, **14:** 19, 21, 16, 14
electrolyte **1:** 31, **2:** 22, 23, **4:** 11, **6:** 12, 13, 14, 15, 33, **7:** 19, **10:** 29, **12:** 9, 18, **13:** 30, 31, **14:** 19
electrolytic cell **7:** 18, 19, 43
electron **1:** 36, 38, 39, **5:** 16, **6:** 10, 12, 13, **9:** 34, 35, **10:** 20, **15:** 6, 7, 8, **16:** 4, 11, 16
electron shell **14:** 6, **16:** 5
electronics **9:** 36
electroplating **4:** 37, **7:** 26
electrostatic precipitators **13:** 23
element **1–15:** 4, **16–18:** 4
   boiling point **16:** 16
   colour **16:** 15
   density **16:** 16
   melting point **16:** 16
   name **16:** 15
elemental, gases **16:** 11
elemental, state **16:** 4
elements
   origin of **15:** 7
   extraction from their compounds **16:** 14
   relative abundance **16:** 4
emerald **4:** 36, **9:** 12, 22, **12:** 10
emery **7:** 6
emitter **9:** 36
emulsion **4:** 38, **5:** 32, **14:** 43
enriched uranium **15:** 25, 33
environmental damage **11:** 43

environmental impact **8:** 42–43
Epsom salts **13:** 32
equations **1–15:** 46–47, **16–18:** 56–57
Er *see* erbium
erbium (Er) **16:** 50
Es *see* einsteinium
esters **1:** 30, **8:** 29, 41
ethane **8:** 28
ethanol **8:** 28
ethyl acetate **8:** 29
ethylene **1:** 14, **8:** 27, 29, 32, 33, **13:** 40, **14:** 10, 22, 23
ethylene glycol **8:** 37, **12:** 36, 37
ethyl ethanoate **8:** 29, 31
ethyne **8:** 29
Eu *see* europium
europium (Eu) **16:** 51
evaporated **14:** 8
evaporation **2:** 11, 12, 13
exothermic **1:** 24, **14:** 12
exothermic reaction **2:** 34, 35, **12:** 14, 36
explosives **14:** 24, **11:** 24–29, 36
extrusion **7:** 20, 33

F

F *see* fluorine
fallout, nuclear **15:** 39
fast reactor core **15:** 33
fat **1:** 30, 32, **2:** 35, **8:** 29
Fe *see* iron
feldspar **2:** 8, 41, **7:** 7, 10, **9:** 10, 11, 26, 28
Fermi, Enrico **15:** 33
fermium (Fm) **16:** 52
ferric hydroxide **1:** 33, **4:** 14
ferric oxide **4:** 11
ferrocyanide **4:** 15
ferrous **4:** 14
ferrous hydroxide **4:** 15
fertilizer **1:** 16, 24, 26, **2:** 5, 40, **11:** 12, 13, 20–21, 36, **13:** 17, 29, 43
film badge **15:** 12
fire extinguishers **7:** 38, **8:** 15
fireworks **11:** 26
firing **9:** 28
fission **15:** 28–29, 34
fission bomb **15:** 38
fixing **5:** 32
fixing nitrogen **11:** 16–19
flame retardants **12:** 35
float glass **9:** 40–41
flocculate **3:** 25
flotation **5:** 10, 11
flowstone **3:** 14
fluorescence **14:** 9
fluorescent lights **6:** 35, 42
fluorescent tube **1:** 42, **2:** 38, 39
fluoride **14:** 4, 5, 37
fluorine (F) **See Vol. 14 and Vol. 16:** 53; **1:** 8, **8:** 33, **12:** 10
fluorite **14:** 9
fluoroethylene **14:** 23
fluorspar **3:** 8, **14:** 36
flux **6:** 17, 25, **10:** 42, **14:** 36
Fm *see* fermium
food chain **6:** 39
fool's gold **4:** 18, **13:** 13
forged **4:** 28
formaldehyde **8:** 28
formalin **8:** 28
Fort Knox **5:** 41

fossil **3:** 11
fossil fuels **3:** 13, **8:** 11, 12, **13:** 5, 16
fossy jaw **11:** 38
Fr *see* francium
fractional distillation **11:** 8, 9, **12:** 17
fractionation **8:** 24–27
fractionation column **8:** 25, **11:** 8
fractionation tower **1:** 14, **8:** 26, 27
fractions **8:** 25, 26
framework silicate **9:** 14, 15
francium (Fr) **17:** 4
Frasch process **13:** 16, 17
Frasch, Herman **13:** 16
freezing point, water **2:** 24
freon **14:** 38
froth flotation process **6:** 8, **10:** 11
fucus red **6:** 38
fuel **1:** 6, 7
fuel element **15:** 26
fuel rod **15:** 5, 33, 34, 35
fuming nitric acid **1:** 26, **6:** 28
fungicide **5:** 22, 23, **6:** 24, 25, **14:** 28
furnace **4:** 30
fused silica **9:** 38
fusion **1:** 6, 7, **15:** 30–31
fusion bomb **15:** 38

G

Ga *see* gallium
gadolinium (Gd) **17:** 5
galena **10:** 6, 7, 30, **13:** 12, 24
gallium (Ga) **17:** 6
gallium arsenide **6:** 42
galvanic cell **6:** 13
Galvani, Luigi **6:** 11, 16
galvanized iron **4:** 10
galvanizing **6:** 16–17, **12:** 32, 33
gamma radiation **15:** 8, 9, 15, 42
gamma rays **15:** 8
gangue **5:** 11, **6:** 9, **10:** 11, 12
garnet **4:** 40, **9:** 20
garnetiferous mica-schist **9:** 20
gas **1:** 4
gas oil **1:** 14
gasoline **1:** 14, **8:** 26, 27, **10:** 4, 32
Gd *see* gadolinium
Ge *see* germanium
geiger counter (Geiger–Müller tube) **15:** 12, 13, 21
Geiger, Hans **15:** 12
gelatin **5:** 32
gelatinous precipitate **4:** 15, **13:** 36
gemstone **7:** 8, 9, **9:** 12, 13, **12:** 10
germanium (Ge) **17:** 7
geysers **3:** 17, **13:** 9
gilding metals **5:** 18
glass **2:** 30, 40, **3:** 22, **4:** 40, **9:** 15, 23, 30, 38, 40, 41, **10:** 26, 27
glass-ceramic **9:** 30
Glauber's salt **13:** 32, 33
glaze **4:** 38, **10:** 24, 25
global warming **8:** 12
glucinium *see* beryllium
glucose **5:** 34, **8:** 10, 11, 18, **12:** 15
glycerol **1:** 32, **2:** 35
glycerol trinitrate **8:** 6, **11:** 27
goiter **14:** 40
gold (Au) **See Vol. 5 and Vol. 17:** 8–9; **6:** 8, 37, 39, **9:** 16, **10:** 7, 11, **11:** 37
gold leaf **5:** 40

gold plating **5:** 43
gold rush **5:** 37, 38
Goodyear, Charles **8:** 35, **13:** 38
grains **9:** 21
granite **2:** 8, 41, **7:** 6, 10, **9:** 11, 20, 22, 23, **15:** 18, 23
graphite **7:** 19, **8:** 8, 9, 22, **14:** 18, 19, **16:** 10
green gold **5:** 42
Greenhouse Effect **7:** 41, **8:** 12, 42
greenhouse gas **7:** 40
green vitriol **13:** 32
groups (Periodic Table) **16:** 5, 8
   see also Periodic Table
Guinea **7:** 11
guncotton **11:** 27
gunpowder **2:** 41, **11:** 26, **13:** 40, 41
gypsum **3:** 8, 30, **11:** 43, **13:** 12, 13, 32

H

H *see* hydrogen
Ha (hahnium) *see* dubnium
Haber-Bosch process **1:** 16, 17, **11:** 16
hafnium (Hf) **17:** 10
hahnium (Ha) *see* dubnium
half-life **15:** 16–17, 18
halides **5:** 33, **14:** 8
halite **2:** 8, 9, **14:** 8, 9
Hall, Charles Martin **7:** 12
Hall–Héroult process **7:** 19
halogens **2:** 40, **8:** 23, **14:** 4, 5, 6, 22
halothane **14:** 5
hard water **3:** 38, 40
hassium (Hs) **17:** 11
He *see* helium
heart **2:** 41
heat conduction **5:** 15
heavy water **16:** 14
helium (He) **See Vol. 1 and Vol. 17:** 12; **15:** 25, 30, 42
hematite **4:** 12, 13, 15, **12:** 11
hemoglobin **12:** 15
Henckel, Johann **6:** 8
herbicides **8:** 42
Héroult, Paul L. T. **7:** 12
hexagonal crystal **9:** 10, 22
hexandioic acid **8:** 36
hexan-dioyl chloride **8:** 38
Hf *see* hafnium
Hg *see* mercury
high-level waste **15:** 40
Hiroshima **15:** 38
Ho *see* holmium
Hoffman's Voltameter **1:** 10, 11, **12:** 18
holmium (Ho) **17:** 13
hornblende **9:** 24, 43
hot springs **3:** 17
Hs *see* hassium
Hs (wolfram) *see* tungsten
hydrated **13:** 35
hydrated, lime **3:** 24
hydrocarbons **8:** 6, 24–25, 29, **14:** 23
hydrochloric acid **1:** 12, 13, 18, 22–23, 28, 34, 35, **3:** 34, 43, **6:** 11, 28, **8:** 15, **11:** 36, **14:** 10, 11, 13, 15, 17, 22, 23, 32, 33, 34, 35
hydroelectric power **7:** 13

hydrofluoric acid **14:** 37
hydrogen (H) **See Vol. 1 and
Vol. 16:** 14; **17:** 14–15, **2:** 6,
27, 42, **3:** 7, 34, **4:** 41, **8:** 6,
11: 16, 17, 37, **12:** 8, 18, 19,
38, **13:** 26, **14:** 19, 21, 22, 32,
15: 30, 38
hydrogen bomb **15:** 21
hydrogen bonding **1:** 8–9, 10, 11
hydrogen chloride **1:** 22, **14:** 13,
32, 33, 34
hydrogen fluoride **14:** 37
hydrogen gas **6:** 11
hydrogen ions **1:** 10, 20, 32, 34, 36,
12: 9, 19
hydrogen peroxide **12:** 21
hydrogen sulfide **1:** 27, **2:** 33,
4: 18, **5:** 29, 34, **6:** 40, **13:** 4,
10, 16, 24–25, 25, 37
hydrogen-3 (tritium) **15:** 17
hydrometer **13:** 31
hydrophilic **2:** 37
hydrophobic **2:** 37
hydrothermal deposits **5:** 36, **10:** 6
hydrothermal veins **5:** 30, **6:** 6
hydrothermal vents **13:** 8
hydrous **4:** 13
hydroxide ions **1:** 10, 11, 20, 32,
34, **3:** 25, 29, **12:** 9
hypochlorous acid **14:** 17

I

I *see* iodine
ice **1:** 8
ice, prevention **2:** 24
Iceland Spar **3:** 8
igneous rock **9:** 11, 18, 20, 21, 23,
25, **15:** 18
In *see* indium
incandescent lights **1:** 42, 43,
11: 11
incendiary device **11:** 40
indicator **1:** 21, 35, **2:** 6, 7, **4:** 6,
11: 15, **12:** 18
indium (In) **17:** 16
induction period **12:** 36, 37
inert **1:** 39
inert gas **1:** 36, 38
infrared radiation **10:** 20
inner transition metals *see* **16:** 8
Periodic Table
inorganic chemicals **8:** 5, **16:** 13
insoluble **1:** 32
insulator **9:** 34
intermediate level waste **15:** 40
internal combustion engine **8:** 16,
12: 40
iodine (I) **See Vol. 14 and
Vol. 17:** 17
iodine-131 **15:** 43
ion **1:** 11, 34, 36, **2:** 22, 23, 27,
3: 29, 41, **4:** 19, 23, **6:** 13,
11: 43, **15:** 12, **1–15:** 47,
16–18: 57
ionization **15:** 12
ionize **12:** 9
ionized **1:** 11
ions **7:** 18, **9:** 26, 38
Ir *see* iridium
iridium (Ir) **See Vol. 17:** 18; **5:** 28
iron (Fe) **See Vol. 4 and Vol. 17:**
19–20; **1:** 26, **3:** 36, **6:** 16,
7: 24, **9:** 29, 41, 43, **10:** 38,
39, **11:** 17, **12:** 26, 27, 30, 34

iron chloride **4:** 14, 15
iron filings **4:** 7
iron foundry **4:** 29
iron hydroxide **4:** 11, 14, 15,
12: 31
iron ore **4:** 13, 17, 22, 25, 27
iron oxide **7:** 16, **8:** 17, **9:** 13, 18,
19, **11:** 42, **12:** 11, 23, 26,
32, 34
iron oxides **4:** 11, 12, 13, 14, 15,
16, 22, 24, 27, 30, 40
iron sulfate **4:** 7, 15, **13:** 15, 32
iron sulfide **4:** 18, 19, 21,
13: 15, 24
iron III compounds **4:** 14
iron III hydroxide **1:** 33, **4:** 11, 14
iron II compounds **4:** 14
iron II hydroxide **4:** 15
irradiation **15:** 42–43
irrigation **2:** 20, 21
isoprene **8:** 35
isotope **11:** 6, **15:** 4, 7

J

jade **9:** 12, 24
Jamaica **7:** 11
jasper **9:** 13
jet engines **9:** 30
jewelry **5:** 28, 40, **8:** 8
junction diode **9:** 34, 35

K

K *see* potassium
kaolinite **7:** 7, **9:** 26, 28, 29
karst **3:** 11
Kellner, Karl **2:** 26
kerosene **1:** 14, **8:** 26, 27, **12:** 38
key facts, explanation **16:** 15
kidneys **2:** 19, 41
kiln **9:** 28, 29
KLEA **14:** 39
knocking **10:** 32
Kr *see* krypton
Krugerrand **5:** 41
krypton (Kr) **See Vol. 1 and
Vol. 17:** 21
krypton-92 **15:** 28
kyanite **9:** 21

L

La *see* lanthanum
lampblack **8:** 22
lanthanides, lanthanide series **16:** 8
see also Periodic Table
lanthanum (La) **17:** 22
laterite **4:** 17, **7:** 11
latex **8:** 34
lather **3:** 38
lattice **5:** 16
lava **3:** 8, **9:** 11, 15, 21, 23, 25
Lawes, John **13:** 43
lawrencium (Lr) **17:** 23
lead (Pb) **See Vol. 10 and Vol.
17:** 24–25; **6:** 8, 21, **13:** 30,
15: 9, 10, 11
lead-acid battery **6:** 13, **10:** 28, 29,
13: 30–31
lead carbonate **10:** 7, 24
lead chamber process **10:** 17
lead chromate **4:** 39
lead dioxide **10:** 18, 28, 29, **12:** 22,
13: 30
lead IV oxide **10:** 18

leaded fuel **10:** 32
leaded glass **10:** 23
lead flashing **10:** 23
lead hydroxide **10:** 31
lead in fuels **10:** 32
lead monoxide **10:** 8, 10, 18, 21,
12: 22
lead nitrate **4:** 39, **10:** 20, 21,
11: 32, 33, **13:** 24
lead oxide **10:** 18, 26, 27, 28, 29
lead pipes **10:** 22
lead poisoning **10:** 14, 31
lead shot **10:** 14, 15
lead silicate **10:** 24
lead sulfate **10:** 7, 16, 24, 28, 29,
13: 32
lead sulfide **10:** 7, 10, 13, 30,
13: 12, 24
lead II oxide **10:** 8, 18
Leblanc, Nicolas **2:** 28
Leclanché cell **6:** 14
Leclanché, Georges **6:** 14
legumes **11:** 18
Les Baux **7:** 11
leukemia **15:** 23, 27
Li *see* lithium
Liberty Bell **5:** 21
light **14:** 7
light-emitting diode (LED)
9: 34, 35
lighthouse **6:** 31
lightning **11:** 6, 7, 22
lignin **8:** 18
lime **1:** 32, **2:** 29, **3:** 22, 24, **4:** 30,
7: 16, **11:** 14, **13:** 34, 42
lime glass **9:** 38, 39
limescale **3:** 16, 38
limestone **1:** 29, 34, **2:** 28, 29, **3:** 4,
10, 12, 19, 20, **4:** 24, 26, 31,
8: 10, **9:** 38, **10:** 7, **12:** 26
limestone rock **14:** 35
limewater **3:** 7, 26
limonite **4:** 13, 15
liquefied petroleum gas (LPG) **8:** 27
liquid air **12:** 17
liquid crystal display (LCD) **9:** 37
liquid nitrogen **11:** 8, 9
litharge **10:** 8, 18
lithium (Li) **17:** 26
litmus **1:** 21, **14:** 15
litmus paper **1:** 20
lode **5:** 30, 36, **10:** 34, 35
lodestone **4:** 12
low-level waste **15:** 41
Lr *see* lawrencium
Lu *see* lutetium
lubricating oil **1:** 14
lutetium (Lu) **17:** 27

M

Macintosh, Charles **8:** 35
magma **5:** 30, **6:** 6, **9:** 16, 21, 23,
25, 29, 43, **10:** 6, 34
magma chamber **9:** 43
magnesium (Mg) **See Vol. 3 and
Vol. 17:** 28–29; **1:** 18, 36,
4: 6, 22, **6:** 22, **7:** 25, **9:** 26,
11: 37, **12:** 33
magnesium carbonate **3:** 37, 43
magnesium hydroxide **1:** 32,
3: 42, 43
magnesium ions **3:** 34, 40
magnesium oxide **3:** 37

magnesium ribbon **3:** 34, 37
magnesium silicate **9:** 27
magnesium sulfate **13:** 32
magnetic flea **4:** 39
magnetic properties **4:** 20
magnetite **4:** 12
malachite **5:** 7
mallee **2:** 17
manganese (Mn) **See Vol. 4 and
Vol. 17:** 30; **7:** 22, **9:** 20, 29,
41, 43
manganese carbonate **4:** 42
manganese chloride **14:** 11
manganese dioxide **6:** 15
manganese nodules **4:** 41
manganese oxide **4:** 40, 41, 43
manganese sulfate **4:** 42
manganese sulfide **4:** 40
mangrove **2:** 16, 17
manure **11:** 20
marble **3:** 4, 18
Marram grass **2:** 17
massicot **10:** 18, **12:** 22
matches **11:** 38, 40, 41, **14:** 25
Md *see* mendelevium
medicines **13:** 42
meitnerium (Mt) **17:** 31
membrane **2:** 15, 27
"memory" brass **5:** 19
Mendeleev, Dmitri Ivanovich
16: 5, 6, **17:** 7, 32, **18:** 11, 17
mendelevium (Md) **17:** 32
meniscus **6:** 30
mercuric chloride **6:** 32
mercuric chromate **6:** 29
mercuric nitrate **6:** 28, 29
mercuric oxide **6:** 32
mercuric sulfide **6:** 38
mercurochrome **6:** 32, 38
mercurous chloride **6:** 32
mercury (Hg) **See Vol. 6 and
Vol. 17:** 33–34; **1:** 37, **5:** 35,
42, **7:** 22, **11:** 37, **14:** 18
mercury amalgam **14:** 19
mercury battery **6:** 32
mercury cathode cell **6:** 33,
14: 18, 19
mercury cell **6:** 15, 33
mercury poisoning **6:** 38
mercury vapor lamps **6:** 34
metalloids **16:** 8 *see also* Periodic
Table
metal oxides **1:** 32
metals **1:** 12, 32, 36, **2:** 6, 42, **3:** 6,
9: 20, 26, 34, **16:** 8 *see also*
Periodic Table
metamorphic rock **9:** 20, 23, 24
meteorites **4:** 12
methane **8:** 6, 24, 28
methanol **1:** 4
methyl benzene **13:** 10, **14:** 7
methylene chloride **14:** 31
methyl group **9:** 32
methylmercury **6:** 39
methyl orange **1:** 21, 35
Mg *see* magnesium
mica **7:** 7, **9:** 26
microchip **9:** 37
microcrystalline **9:** 14
micronutrient **15:** 7
microorganisms **14:** 16
microprocessors **9:** 36
mild steel **4:** 32, 33, 34
Milk of Magnesia **3:** 42

mineral **2:** 9, **3:** 8, 15 , **8:** 8, **9:** 9, 11, 12, 20, 21, 43 , **12:** 10, **13:** 12–13

mineral acid **1:** 18, 19, 24, 25, **13:** 26, 27

mining **2:** 12, **5:** 10, 30, 36, 38, **7:** 10–11, **10:** 6, 7, 12, 34, 36

mirrors **5:** 34, 5

mixtures **4:** 20, **16:** 4, 12

Mn *see* manganese

Mo *see* molybdenum

molecule **2:** 19, 27, **9:** 11, **12:** 9, **13:** 6

molybdenum (Mo) **See Vol. 17:** 35; **4:** 34, **13:** 12

monoclinic crystal **13:** 10, 11, 13

monomer **13:** 38, 39, **8:** 32, 33

monoxide gas **10:** 10

mordant **7:** 36

mortar **3:** 22

MOSFETS (metal oxide semiconductor field effect transistors) **9:** 36

Mt *see* meitnerium

mullite **9:** 29

murex **14:** 42

muriatic acid **14:** 34

muscles **2:** 41

muscovite **7:** 6, **9:** 26, 27

mustard gas **13:** 40, **14:** 26

N

N *see* nitrogen

Na *see* sodium

Nagasaki **15:** 38, 39

nail-polish **8:** 29, 31

nail-polish remover **8:** 29, 31

naphtha **1:** 14

napping **9:** 14

native copper **5:** 7

native elements **16:** 10

native gold **5:** 36

native metal **4:** 12, 13

native silver **5:** 30

natural gas **8:** 10, 13, 24

Nb *see* niobium

Nd *see* neodymium

negative terminal **6:** 14

Ne *see* neon

neodymium (Nd) **17:** 36

neon (Ne) **See Vol.1 and Vol. 17:** 37

"neon" lights **2:** 39, **17:** 37

neon tubes **1:** 40

neptunium (Np) **17:** 38

nerve cells **2:** 18

neutral **1:** 20, 34

neutralization **1:** 34–35, **2:** 31, 33

neutralize **3:** 21, 25, 43

neutron radiation **15:** 8, 9

neutrons **15:** 7, 8, 28, **16:** 4, 5

Ni *see* nickel

nickel (Ni) **See Vol. 17:** 39; **4:** 34, 36, 41, **5:** 40, **7:** 22

nickel–cadmium cell **6:** 41

nickel sulfide **13:** 12, 25

nielsborhium (Ns) *see* dubnium

Nightingale, Florence **14:** 16

niobium (Nb) **17:** 40

niobium-101 **15:** 29

nitrate fertilizer **11:** 20

nitrates **11:** 20

nitric acid **1:** 18, 22–26, 27, 37, **5:** 14, 26, **6:** 28, **7:** 33, **11:** 5, 6, 7, 13, 30, 33, 36–37

nitric acid, fuming **5:** 14

nitric oxide **1:** 26, **10:** 17, **11:** 7, 34, 35, 37, **12:** 42, 43

nitrifying bacteria **11:** 23

nitrocellulose **11:** 27

nitrogen (N) **See Vol. 11 and Vol. 17:** 41–42

nitrogen **1:** 8, 16, 17, 42, **8:** 6, 36, **12:** 17, **15:** 10

nitrogen cycle **11:** 22–23

nitrogen dioxide **1:** 26, 37, **6:** 28, **10:** 17, 21, **11:** 5, 7, 30–33, 34, 35, 37, **12:** 13, 41, 42, 43

nitrogen-fixing bacteria **11:** 18

nitrogen-fixing nodules **11:** 19

nitrogen oxides **7:** 40, 43

nitroglycerin **8:** 6, **11:** 27

nitrous oxide **11:** 34

No *see* nobelium

Nobel, Alfred **11:** 27

nobelium (No) **17:** 43

noble gases **1:** 5, 38–39, **11:** 8, **16:** 11

noble metals **5:** 28, **6:** 28

nonmetals **16:** 8 *see also* Periodic Table

nonstick **14:** 37

Novocaine **14:** 5

NO$_x$ **11:** 34–35

Np *see* neptunium

Ns (nielsborhium) *see* dubnium

n-type region **9:** 34

nuclear accidents **15:** 36–37

nuclear energy (nuclear power) **1:** 6, **15:** 32–33

nuclear fusion **1:** 6

nuclear power station **15:** 32

nuclear reactions **15:** 4, 7

nuclear reactors **15:** 34–35

nuclear waste **15:** 40

nuclear weapons **15:** 38

nucleus **15:** 4, 6, 7, 8

nugget **5:** 36, 37

nutrients **2:** 16, 18, 20

nylon **8:** 31, 36, 37, 38, 39

O

O *see* oxygen

obsidian **9:** 15

ocher **4:** 15

octane **1:** 14

octane numbers **10:** 32

Oersted, Hans Christian **7:** 12

oil **8:** 10, 13

oils **1:** 30

oil spill **8:** 42

oil-storage tanks **3:** 37

oil-storage tanks **3:** 37

olivine **9:** 21, 27

oolitic limestone **3:** 10

opal **9:** 14

oral rehydration **2:** 18

ore **3:** 10, **4:** 13, 17, 18, 24, 27, 36, **5:** 8, **6:** 6, 8, **7:** 10, 11, 13, **10:** 6, 8, 10, 34, 35, 36, **13:** 12, 15

ore-flotation **5:** 11

organic acid **1:** 18, 19, 30, 31, **2:** 30, **3:** 39

organic chemicals **8:** 5, 20, 42, 43

organic compounds **8:** 28, **16:** 13

organic solvents **14:** 7

organochloride **14:** 28, 29

Os *see* osmium

oscillator **9:** 37

osmium (Os) **17:** 44

osmosis **2:** 14–15, 16, 17, 19, 25

oxalic acid **1:** 30

oxidation **3:** 35, **4:** 11, 13, 23, 27, 31, **6:** 14, **8:** 10, 11, 18, **9:** 29, **12:** 6, 14, 24, 25, 26, 34, 36, **14:** 11, 14, 15, 16

oxide **4:** 8, 9, 17, **7:** 8, 14, 24, 26, 33, 34, 35, **10:** 8, **12:** 10, 22, 30

oxidization **10:** 11

oxidize **4:** 8, 16, 27, 30, 31, 40, **13:** 20

oxidizing agent **4:** 42, 43, **6:** 28, **11:** 30, **12:** 20, 37

oxyacetylene **12:** 16, 39

oxygen (O) **See Vol. 12 and Vol. 17:** 45–47; **1:** 8, 10, 11, **2:** 43; **4:** 9, 11, 12, 14, 16, 22, 23, 30, 40, 41, **7:** 6, 38, 39, **8:** 10, 11, 18, 28, **9:** 9, 10, 26, 33, 38, **11:** 7, 9, 33, 35, **13:** 14, 14, 24, 25

oxygen cycle **12:** 14

oxygen, test for the presence **17:** 47

ozone **11:** 35, **12:** 6, 12, 13, 42, 43, **14:** 38, 39

ozone layer **14:** 38

P

P *see* phosphorus

Pa *see* protactinium

painkillers **14:** 5

paint **6:** 19, **10:** 24, 25, **12:** 21, 32

paint stripper **14:** 31

palladium (Pd) **See Vol. 17:** 48; **5:** 28, **12:** 41

panning **5:** 39

paraquat **14:** 29

Parkes, Alexander **8:** 31

Parkes process **10:** 10, 11

patina **1:** 29, **5:** 4, 6, 27

Pb *see* lead

PBB *see* polybrominated biphenyls

PCBs *see* polychlorinated biphenyls

Pd *see* palladium

pearl **3:** 4

pentaerythrite tetranitrate **11:** 27

perchloric acid **12:** 39

percolate **3:** 14, 15

Periodic Law **16:** 5

Periodic Table **1–15:** 44–45, **16:** 4, 5, 6–7, 8, 54–55, **17–18:** 54–55

periods (Periodic Table) **16:** 5 *see also* Periodic Table

permanent hardness **3:** 38

pesticide **2:** 30, **6:** 24, 25, **8:** 42, **13:** 42, **14:** 28, 29

Pete Bog **15:** 18

PETN **11:** 27

petrochemical plant **8:** 26, 29

petrochemicals **8:** 26

petroleum **8:** 7, 24, **14:** 22

Pewter **10:** 40

pH **1:** 20, 21, 28

phenolphthalein **1:** 21, **2:** 6, 7, **11:** 15

phosgene **14:** 26

phosphates **11:** 42

phosphine gas **11:** 39

phosphor **6:** 35, 42, 43

phosphor bronze **5:** 20

phosphoric acid **10:** 24, **11:** 42, **12:** 32

phosphorus (P) **See Vol. 11 and Vol. 17:** 49–50; **3:** 40, **5:** 20, **9:** 34, **10:** 41

phosphorus oxide **11:** 39

phosphorus, red **14:** 25

photochemical smog **12:** 42

photoelectric cell **6:** 5, 42, 43

photoelectric properties **10:** 20

photographer's hypo **5:** 33, **13:** 33, **14:** 43

photographic films **8:** 41

photography **5:** 32, **14:** 42, 43

photon **6:** 43

photosynthesis **8:** 10, 11, **12:** 6, 14

photovoltaic cell **6:** 42

pickling **2:** 25

piezoelectric effect **9:** 37

pig iron **4:** 24, 27, 28, 30

pigment **4:** 38, **6:** 24, 40

pitchblende **15:** 22, 24

placer deposit **5:** 39, **10:** 36

plaster **5:** 31

Plaster of Paris **3:** 31, **13:** 12, 32

plastic **8:** 30–31, 43

plastic, properties **8:** 30

plastics **14:** 22, 23

plastic sulfur **13:** 7

platinum (Pt) **See Vol. 17:** 51; **5:** 28, **10:** 33, **11:** 37, **12:** 41, **14:** 20

playa lakes **14:** 8, 9

playas **2:** 10

plumbing **10:** 22

plutonium (Pu) **See Vol. 17:** 52; **15:** 26, 34, 35, 38

Pm *see* promethium

Po *see* polonium

poison **6:** 24, **11:** 38

poison gas **14:** 26

pollutants **7:** 42, **14:** 16

pollute **11:** 20

pollution **2:** 20–21, 33, **3:** 13, **10:** 12, **12:** 40, 42, **13:** 18, 19, 22, 23, **15:** 20

polonium (Po) **See Vol. 17:** 53; **15:** 23,

polonium-210 **15:** 17

polybrominated biphenyls **14:** 29

polychlorinated biphenyls **14:** 28

polychloroethylene **8:** 33, **14:** 10, 22, 23

polyester **8:** 31, 36, 37, 40, 41

polyethylene **8:** 31, 32, **14:** 23

polyfluoroethylene **14:** 22, 23

polymer **2:** 26, **9:** 33, **13:** 38, 39, **14:** 22, 9

polymerization **8:** 32–39, **13:** 39, **14:** 22, **9:** 4, 32

polymers **8:** 30–41

polystyrene **8:** 31, 33

polytetrafluoroethylene **8:** 31, 33, **14:** 36, 37

polyvinyl benzene **8:** 33

polyvinyl chloride **8:** 33, *see also* polychloroethylene

polyvinyl fluoride *see* polyfluoroethylene

porous **3:** 10, **4:** 9

porous bronze **5:** 20

Portland cement **3:** 23
positive terminal **6:** 14
potash **2:** 40
potash salts **2:** 41
potassium (K) **See Vol. 2 and Vol. 18:** 4–5; **4:** 6, **7:** 6, **9:** 11, 26
potassium carbonate **2:** 40
potassium chlorate **11:** 41, **14:** 24, 25
potassium chloride **6:** 13, **14:** 11
potassium chromate **4:** 38, 39, **6:** 29
potassium dichromate **4:** 38
potassium-40 **15:** 11
potassium hydroxide **2:** 42, **4:** 43, **6:** 15
potassium iodide **14:** 41
potassium manganate **4:** 42, 43, **14:** 15
potassium metal **2:** 42
potassium nitrate **1:** 27, **2:** 40, 41, 42, 43, **4:** 42, 43, **11:** 4, 21, 26, 36, **13:** 41
potassium nitrite **2:** 43
potassium permanganate **4:** 42, 43, **12:** 21, 36, 37, **14:** 10
potassium phosphate **2:** 40
potassium sulfate **2:** 40
pottery **9:** 28
power stations **13:** 22
Pr *see* praseodymium
praseodymium (Pr) **18:** 6
precious metal **5:** 28, **10:** 16
precipitate **3:** 7, 16, 26, 38, **4:** 39, 41, **13:** 23, 36, 37
precipitation **3:** 14, **14:** 8
preservatives **13:** 42
preserving **2:** 25
primary dry battery **6:** 15
printed circuits **5:** 17
procaine hydrochloride **14:** 5
promethium (Pm) **18:** 7
protactinium (Pa) **18:** 8
protein chain **8:** 36
proteins **8:** 10, 18, 36, **11:** 4
proton number **16:** 5
protons **15:** 7, 8, **16:** 4, 5
prussian blue **4:** 15
Pt *see* platinum
PTFE **8:** 33
p-type region **9:** 34
Pu *see* plutonium
PVC **8:** 33 *see also* polychloroethylene
PVF *see* polyfluoroethylene
pyrite **4:** 18, 19, 21, **10:** 17, **13:** 12, 13, 15, 16, 24
pyrolusite **4:** 41
pyroxenes **9:** 24

Q

quartz **4:** 18, **9:** 10, 11, 12, 13, 14, 15, 18, 26, 37, 38, **12:** 10
quartzite **9:** 16
quicklime **3:** 20, 22, 24
quicksilver **6:** 26

R

Ra *see* radium
radium (Ra) **18:** 9
radiated **7:** 30
radiation **1:** 7, **10:** 26, 31, **15:** 8, 42, 43

radiation sickness **15:** 42
radiation therapy **15:** 43
radioactive decay **15:** 16
radioactive decay, graph **15:** 16
radioactive elements **15:** 4, 6, 26–27, **16:** 8
radioactive isotopes **1:** 42
radioactive tracers **15:** 20–21
radioactivity **15:** 5, 7, 8–9
radioisotopes **15:** 17
radium **1:** 43, **15:** 5, 15, 17, 22–23, 36
radon (Rn) **See Vol. 1 and Vol. 18:** 10; **15:** 14, 23, **16:** 10, Ramsay, Sir William **1:** 38
rate of chemical reaction **2:** 24
Ravenscroft **10:** 22
rayon **8:** 38
Rb *see* rubidium
RDX **11:** 27, 28
Re *see* rhenium
reaction **3:** 6
reactivity **2:** 7, 42, **4:** 7, **5:** 15, 29, 41, **6:** 16, **7:** 6, 14, 24–25, **10:** 16, **11:** 10, **14:** 5, 6, 41
reactivity series **1:** 36, **2:** 7, **3:** 36, **4:** 6, 40, 41, **5:** 15, 29, 41, **6:** 11, 16, **7:** 24, **10:** 16, 39, **12:** 28
recycling **7:** 40
red gold **5:** 42
red lead **10:** 18, 24, **12:** 22
red mud **7:** 17, 42
red mud pollution **7:** 42
red phosphorus **11:** 38, 40–41
redox reaction **12:** 24, 25
reduced **4:** 24, **10:** 8
reducing **14:** 14
reducing agent **4:** 25, 27, **5:** 8, 34, **8:** 16, 17, **13:** 20, 24
reduction **4:** 11, 23, **5:** 8, 9, **7:** 18, **12:** 24, 25, 26, **13:** 20
refining **5:** 12, 31, 39, **6:** 9, 37, **7:** 12, 18–19, **12:** 28, 29
refining metals **1:** 4
reflection **7:** 30
refrigerants **14:** 38, 39
refrigeration **11:** 12
refrigerator **14:** 38, 39
Reims cathedral **3:** 13
reinforced concrete **4:** 32
relative atomic mass **16:** 7
rem (roentgen equivalent in man) **15:** 43
reprocessing, uranium **15:** 25
resin **3:** 41, **12:** 20
resistors **9:** 37
respiration **8:** 10, **12:** 14
reverse osmosis **2:** 14
Rf *see* rutherfordium
Rh *see* rhodium
rhenium (Re) **18:** 11
Rhizobium **11:** 18
rhodium (Rh) **See Vol. 18:** 12; **5:** 42
rhombic crystal **13:** 5, 10, 11
rhombohedral-shaped crystal **3:** 9
rings **9:** 22
riveting **4:** 28
Rn *see* radon
rocks **9:** 12
rock salt **2:** 8, 10, 12, **14:** 8, 9, 19
Romans **10:** 30
Ru *see* ruthenium

rubber **8:** 34, 35, **9:** 33, **13:** 38
rubidium (Rb) **18:** 13
ruby **4:** 36, **7:** 8, 9, **9:** 13, 22, **12:** 11
rust **4:** 7, 8–11, 35, **7:** 24, **10:** 38, 39, **12:** 30, 32
rust-inhibitor **11:** 42
ruthenium (Ru) **18:** 14
Rutherford, Ernest **15:** 9
rutherfordium (Rf) **18:** 15

S

S *see* sulfur
sacrificial anode **6:** 18, **7:** 25
salicylic acid **1:** 30
saline **2:** 11, 20, **14:** 9
saline drip **2:** 18
saline solution **2:** 9, 18, 19
salinization **2:** 20, 21
salt **1:** 22, 32, 33, 34, **2:** 6, 7, 8–17, 18, 21, 24, 26, 28, 40, **13:** 9, **14:** 8, 9, 19, 34
salt bridge **6:** 13, 14
saltbush **2:** 17
salt deposits **2:** 8
salt dome **2:** 12, **14:** 19, **13:** 8
salt pans **2:** 12, 13, 40
saltpeter **11:** 4, 21, **13:** 41
salt pollution **2:** 20
salts **2:** 40, 41, 42
samarium (Sm) **18:** 16
sand **9:** 38, 40
sand dunes **9:** 19
sandstones **9:** 18
saponification **2:** 34, 36, 37
sapphire **7:** 8, 9, **12:** 10
saturated **3:** 6, 7
Sb *see* antimony
Sc *see* scandium
scale **3:** 10, 39
scandium (Sc) **18:** 17
schist **9:** 20
scrubbing **2:** 33, **13:** 17
scum **3:** 40
Se *see* selenium
seaborgium (Sg) **18:** 18
sea-salt **2:** 13
seawater **2:** 13, **14:** 4, 9, 40, 42
seaweed **14:** 4, 9, 40
secondary battery **6:** 13, **13:** 31
sediment **9:** 18, 21
sedimentary rocks **9:** 18
sediments **2:** 10
selenide **9:** 41
selenium (Se) **See Vol. 18:** 19; **6:** 42
semiconductor **6:** 43, **9:** 34, 35
semimetals *see* metalloids
semipermeable membrane **1:** 15, **2:** 14, 15, 16, 25, **6:** 14, 15
serpentine **9:** 27
sewage systems **14:** 16
Sg *see* seaborgium
shales **7:** 36
shell diagrams **16:** 4, 5
sheet minerals **7:** 7
sheet silicate **9:** 27, 29
Si *see* silicon
silica **4:** 26, **9:** 9, 10, 14, 16, 29, 35, 38, 39, 42, 43, **10:** 26, **11:** 38, **12:** 10
silicate **4:** 40, **9:** 8, 9, 11, 12, 18, 20, 26
silicate groups **9:** 9

silicates **12:** 10
silicon (Si) **See Vol. 9 and Vol. 18:** 20–21; **4:** 29, 30, 34, **6:** 42, **7:** 6, 22, **10:** 41, **12:** 10
silicon bronze **5:** 21
silicon carbide **8:** 5, **9:** 30
silicon chip **9:** 4, 34
silicone **9:** 32, 33
silicon wafer **1:** 42, **9:** 34
silver (Ag) **See Vol. 5 and Vol. 18:** 22–23; **6:** 8, 37, **7:** 31, **10:** 7, 11, **13:** 33
silver bromide **5:** 32, 33, **14:** 42, 43
silver chloride **5:** 32, 33, **14:** 7
silver chloride battery **6:** 15
silvering **5:** 34
silver iodide **5:** 32, 33, **14:** 40, 43
silver oxide battery **6:** 15
silver rush **5:** 30
silver salts **5:** 32
silver sulfide **5:** 29, **13:** 25
sink holes **3:** 12
sinter **3:** 17
sintering **9:** 29
slag **4:** 24, 26, 27, 30, 40, **10:** 10, **12:** 26
slaked lime **3:** 24, 28, **11:** 14
sluice box **5:** 38, **10:** 36
Sm *see* samarium
smelling salts **11:** 12
smelter **7:** 13, 18
smelting **4:** 24–27, **5:** 11, **6:** 8
smithsonite **6:** 6
smog **11:** 34, **12:** 41, 42, **13:** 22
smoke detectors **15:** 15
smoky quartz **9:** 12, 13
Sn *see* tin
soap **1:** 30, 32, **2:** 34, 35, 36–37
soda **2:** 4, 30
soda ash **2:** 29, 30, **7:** 16
soda glass **2:** 39
soda lakes **2:** 41
soda-lime glass **9:** 38
sodium (Na) **See Vol. 2 and Vol. 18:** 24–25; **1:** 36, **7:** 6, **9:** 11, 24, 38
sodium aluminate **2:** 32, **7:** 15, 17
sodium azide **11:** 29
sodium bicarbonate **2:** 28, 29, 30–31, **8:** 14
sodium carbonate **2:** 28–29, 30–31, **7:** 38, **8:** 15, **9:** 39, 40
sodium chlorate **14:** 14, 24, 25
sodium chloride **1:** 32, **2:** 6, 7, 8, 9, 12, 13, 23, 24, 27, 29, 31, **4:** 14, **6:** 33, **9:** 9, **13:** 9, **14:** 4, 8, 9, 19, 25
sodium hydroxide **1:** 30, 32, 34, 35, **2:** 6, 26, 27, 30, 32–35, 36, **4:** 14, 15, **5:** 27, **6:** 33, 41, **7:** 14, 15, 16, **13:** 23, 25, **14:** 14, 19, 20, 21
sodium ion **1:** 34, **2:** 9, 22, **3:** 40, **14:** 8, 20
sodium metal **2:** 6, 7
sodium pellet **2:** 6
sodium peroxydisulfate **13:** 20
sodium, radioactive **15:** 20
sodium stearate **2:** 36
sodium sulfate **13:** 32, 33
sodium sulfide **2:** 33
sodium sulfite **13:** 20
sodium thiosulfate **5:** 33, **13:** 33, **14:** 43

sodium triphosphate **11:** 43
sodium vapor lamps **2:** 4
soil **3:** 12, 24, 28, **4:** 16–17, **7:** 43
soil conditioner **3:** 24, 28
solar cell **6:** 42, **9:** 35
solder **10:** 42, 43
soldered **7:** 20
solder glasses **10:** 27
Soliman's Water **6:** 38
soluble **1:** 32, **9:** 38
solution **2:** 23, 34, **3:** 12, 16, 27,
    4: 7, 15, 17, **7:** 15, 17,
    9: 13, 15
solution mining **2:** 12
Solvay, Ernest **2:** 28
Solvay process **2:** 28–29, 32
solvent **8:** 28, 29, 31, **14:** 7, 30
soot **8:** 22, **14:** 13
SO$_x$ **13:** 22
space suits **7:** 30
spectrum **1:** 38
sphalerite **4:** 18, **6:** 6, **13:** 12
spontaneous combustion **11:** 39,
    12: 36, 37
stable **9:** 10
stainless steel **4:** 34, 35, 36
stalactite **3:** 14
stalagmite **3:** 14, 39
starches **8:** 43
stars **1:** 6–7, **15:** 31
state **1–15:** 46, **16–18:** 56
stationary phase **7:** 35
steam **3:** 24
steel **1:** 22, **4:** 30–35, **6:** 18, **7:** 21,
    25, 33, **10:** 38, **12:** 32
steel furnace **12:** 25
steelmaking **12:** 26
sterling silver **5:** 28
stomach **1:** 28
Stone Age **9:** 14
stratosphere **12:** 12
striations **4:** 18, **9:** 23
strong acid **1:** 18, 19, 20, **13:** 18,
    19, 26
strong alkali **1:** 20
strontium (Sr) **18:** 26
strontium chlorate **14:** 24
strontium-90 **15:** 27, 39, 42
strontium-94 **15:** 29
styrene **8:** 33, 35
styrofoam **8:** 33
Sr *see* strontium
sublimation **8:** 14, 15
sucrose **1:** 24, **8:** 19
sugar **1:** 24, **8:** 10, 19
sugars **12:** 14
sulfates **13:** 12, 32–33, 43
sulfide **10:** 8
sulfides **5:** 6, **13:** 8, 12, 16
sulfites **13:** 18, 32–33, 42
sulfur (S) **See Vol. 13 and Vol.**
    18: 27–28; **4:** 19, 20, 21, 30,
    40, **8:** 34, 35, **10:** 10, 12,
    11: 26
sulfur bridge **13:** 39
sulfur dioxide **2:** 33, **4:** 10, **6:** 8, **7:** 21,
    10: 10, 12, 17, **12:** 13, 29,
    13: 5, 9, 14, 16, 18–23, 28
sulfur, flowers **13:** 7
sulfuric acid **1:** 18, 24–25, 27, 37,
    2: 33, **4:** 18, 19, 42, **6:** 28,
    7: 36, **8:** 19, **10:** 10, 16, 17,
    28, 29, **11:** 36, 42, 43, **13:** 16,
    18, 26–31, 34, 43

sulfuric acid, dilute **5:** 24
sulfurous acid **13:** 18, 19
sulfur oxides **7:** 40, 43
sulfur trioxide **13:** 19, 28, 29
Sun **1:** 6, **15:** 30
supernova **15:** 31
superphosphates **1:** 24, **11:** 42, 43
superphosphate fertilizers **13:** 29
suspension **4:** 38, **13:** 17
swarf **4:** 7
swimming pool **14:** 16, 17
swimming pool disinfectant **14:** 43
switch **6:** 30
symbols, chemical **1–15:** 46–47,
    16: 4, 15, **16–18:** 2, 56–57
synthetic fiber **8:** 38–41
synthetic ivory **8:** 31

T

Ta *see* tantalum
table salt **14:** 4, 9
talc **9:** 26
tantalum (Ta) **18:** 29
tarnish **5:** 29
tarnishing **13:** 25
tartaric acid **1:** 18, 30, **8:** 14
Tb *see* terbium
Tc *see* technetium
Te *see* tellurium
tear gas **14:** 26
technetium (Tc) **See Vol. 18:** 30;
    15: 20
teeth **3:** 5, 33, **14:** 37
Teflon **8:** 31, 33, **14:** 36
telluride **10:** 20, **18:** 31
tellurium (Te) **18:** 31
temperature, effect of salt **2:** 24
tempering **4:** 33
temporary hardness **3:** 38
terbium (Tb) **18:** 32
terephthalic acid **8:** 37
tetraethyl lead **10:** 32
tetrafluoroethylene **8:** 33,
    14: 36, 37
tetrahedron **8:** 8, **9:** 9, 10, **12:** 10
tetraphosphorus trisulfide **11:** 41
Th *see* thorium
thallium (Tl) **18:** 33
thermometer **6:** 31
thermoplastic **8:** 33, **14:** 22
thorium (Th) **18:** 34
thoron **15:** 14
Three Mile Island **15:** 36
thulium (Tm) **18:** 35
Ti *see* titanium
tiger's-eye **9:** 13
tin (Sn) **See Vol. 10 and Vol.**
    18: 36–37; **3:** 36, **5:** 18, 20,
    6: 37, **7:** 4, **9:** 16, 40,
    12: 32, 33
tin can **7:** 33
tincture of iodine **14:** 40
tin dioxide **10:** 35
tin oxide **10:** 34, 35, 36
tin plating **10:** 38, 39, **12:** 33
titanium (Ti) **See Vol. 18:** 38;
    7: 22, **9:** 30, 31, **14:** 20
titration **1:** 34, 35
Tl *see* thallium
Tm *see* thulium
TNT **8:** 6, **11:** 13, 27
topaz **12:** 10
Torricelli, Evangelista **6:** 30
tourmaline **9:** 22, 23

transistor **9:** 36, 37
transition elements **16:** 8 *see also*
    Periodic Table
translucent **9:** 11
transmutation **15:** 10
travertine **3:** 8, 14, 16
trichloroethylene **14:** 30
trinitrotoluene **8:** 6, **11:** 27
tripod **4:** 43
tritium **15:** 8, 17, 21, 30, 38, **17:** 14
tungsten (W) **See Vol. 18:** 39;
    4: 34
tungsten steel **4:** 35
turbines **7:** 23
turpentine **14:** 30

U

U *see* uranium
ultraviolet light **6:** 35, **8:** 30, 33,
    12: 12, **14:** 39
Une (unnilennium) *see* meitnerium
Unh (unnilhexium) *see* seaborgium
Universal Indicator **1:** 20, **12:** 18
unleaded fuel **10:** 33
unnilennium (Une) *see* meitnerium
unnilhexium (Unh) *see* seaborgium
unniloctium (Uno) *see* hassium
unnilpentium (Unp) *see* dubnium
Uno (unniloctium) *see* hassium
Unp (unnilpentium) *see* dubnium
unsaturated hydrocarbons **8:** 29
ununbium (Uub) **18:** 40
ununhexium (Uuh) **18:** 41
unununium (Uuu) **18:** 45
ununnilium (Uun) **18:** 42
ununoctium (Uuo) **18:** 43
ununquadium (Uuq) **18:** 44
u-PVC **8:** 33
uranium (U) **See Vol. 15 and**
    Vol. 18: 46
uranium fission **15:** 28–29
uranium hexafluoride **14:** 36
uranium oxide **15:** 34
uranium-235 **15:** 28, 29
uranium-238 **15:** 11, 17
urea **11:** 13, 23
Uub *see* ununbium
Uuh *see* ununhexium
Uun *see* ununnilium
Uuo *see* ununoctium
Uuq *see* ununquadium
Uuu *see* unununium

V

V *see* vanadium
vanadium (V) **See Vol. 18:** 47;
    4: 34, **12:** 22
vanadium pentoxide **13:** 28
vapor **2:** 38
veins **4:** 18, **5:** 6, 30, 36, **9:** 16
Venus **13:** 9
vermiculite **9:** 26
vinegar **1:** 31
vinyl **8:** 33, **14:** 22
vinyl chloride **8:** 33; *see also*
    chloroethylene
vinyl fluoride *see* fluoroethylene
viscous **9:** 43
vitreous **2:** 9
Volta, Alessandro **6:** 12
Voltage **9:** 34
von Liebig, Justus **5:** 34
vulcanization **8:** 34, 35, **13:** 38–39

W

W *see* tungsten
wafer **9:** 37
wallboard **3:** 30
washing **3:** 40
waste glass **9:** 40
water **1:** 9, 10–11, 28, **2:** 6–7, 10,
    14, 15, 18, 22, 25, 30, 31, 34,
    35, 42, **3:** 38, 40, **4:** 10, 11,
    18, **8:** 36, **9:** 14, 26, 28, 29,
    12: 4, 8, 9, 14, 15, 18, 19, 38
water of crystallization **13:** 35
water supplies **14:** 16
water-softener **3:** 40
waterproof **9:** 33
weak **1:** 29, 31
weak acid **1:** 19, 20, **13:** 18, 19
weak alkali **1:** 20
weather **1:** 29
weathering **3:** 12, 19, **9:** 18, 19,
    20, 21
weedkillers **14:** 24, 29
welding **12:** 39
wet batteries **13:** 30
white gold **5:** 42
white lead **10:** 24, 30
white phosphorus **11:** 38–39
whitewash **3:** 23
wolfram (Hs) *see* tungsten
World War I **8:** 31, **13:** 40, **14:** 26
World War II **15:** 38
wrought bronze **5:** 20
wrought iron **4:** 28, 29

X

Xe *see* xenon
xenon (Xe) **See Vol. 1 and**
    Vol. 18: 48; **15:** 20
xenon-140 **15:** 29
X-rays **10:** 26, 31, **15:** 8, 14, 15, 36

Y

Y *see* yttrium
Yb *see* ytterbium
ytterbium (Yb) **18:** 49
yttrium (Y) **18:** 50

Z

zinc (Zn) **See Vol. 6 and Vol.**
    18: 51–52; **1:** 12, 37, **4:** 10,
    41, **5:** 18, **7:** 25, **10:** 7, 11,
    12: 32, 33, **13:** 8, 26, **14:** 32
zinc–cadmium battery **6:** 13
zinc carbonate **6:** 6, 7
zinc cell **6:** 12, 15
zinc chloride **6:** 17, 25
zinc hydroxide **6:** 41
zinc oxide **6:** 9, 24
zinc sulfate **6:** 9, 12, 25
zinc sulfide **4:** 18, **6:** 6, 9, 25,
    13: 12
zircon **9:** 20, 21
zirconium (Zr) **See Vol. 18:** 53;
    9: 12, 21
Zn *see* zinc
Zr *see* zirconium